HOUGHTON MIFFLIN SOCIAL STUDIES

Oh, California

Reading Support Workbook

HOUGHTON MIFFLIN

Boston • Atlanta • Dallas • Geneva, Illinois • Palo Alto • Princeton

Printed in U. S. A.

ISBN: 0-395-94698-0

23456789-B-02 01 00 99

Table of Contents

Table of Contents (continued)

Table of Contents (continued)

Table of Contents (continued)

Chapter Overview
Geography of California

Fill in the blank spaces below with information from the chapter.

When: Today

Where: California

Who: People of California

Geography of California

California

Location	Regions	Resources
North America	coast	**natural:**
______	Central Valley	soil
western coast	______	______
	______	______
		______
		human:
		______

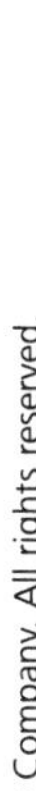

Name: Date:

CHAPTER 1

Lesson 1 Preview

Where on Earth Is California?

(*Oh, California* pp. 4–8)

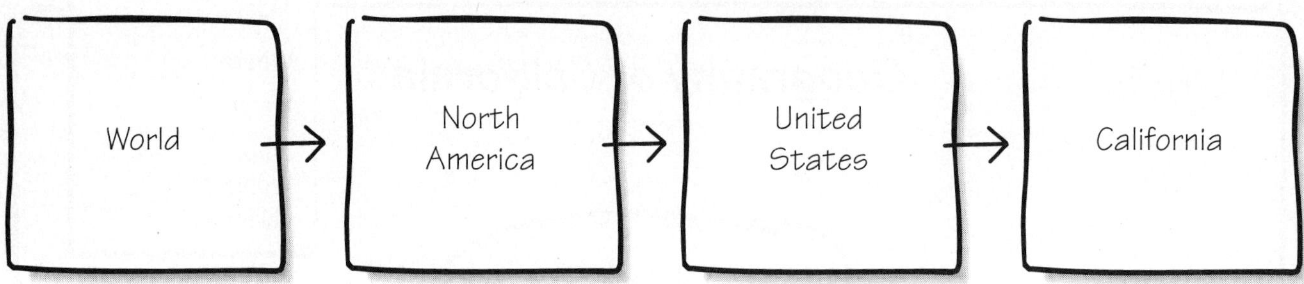

1. **Look at the graphic organizer above. Then read the following descriptions. Circle the letter that tells where California is located.**

   a. California is in South America.
   b. California is outside the United States.

   c. California is outside the United States, but inside the world.
   d. California is on the continent of North America inside the United States.

2. **Look at the map on page 7 of your text. List the names of the states that border California.**

Name: Date:

CHAPTER 1

Lesson 1 Reading Strategy

Where on Earth Is California?

(*Oh, California* pp. 4–8)

Self-Question This reading strategy helps you stay focused on what you read. Ask yourself questions before you read a section. Then read to see if you can find the answer to your questions.

1. **Read the heading "Looking at the Earth" on page 5 and look at the map. Check the question you think this section will answer.**

   ___ How do maps help us look at the earth?

   ___ Which is better—a map or a globe?

   ___ What are the best colors to use in a map?

   Now read the section to see if that question was answered.

2. **Read the heading "Looking at North America" on page 6. Write a question you think this section will answer.**

   ____

   Read the section to see if that question was answered.

3. **Read the heading "Zooming in on California" on page 7 and look closely at the map on page 8. Write a question you think this section will answer. Then read the section and write any answers you find.**

My Question	What I Learned by Reading

CHAPTER 1

Summary also on Audiotape

Lesson 1 Summary
Where on Earth Is California?

(*Oh, California* pp. 4–8)

Thinking Focus: What states, countries, and continents are closest to California?

Looking at the Earth

A **globe** and a map are alike in many ways. Both show the areas of land and the bodies of water found on the earth. Both have lines drawn on them and show the names of oceans and **continents.** But a globe and a map are also different. A globe is a ball, while a map is flat. To see all seven continents on a globe, you must turn the globe around. A world map lets you see all seven continents at once.

[?] In what ways is a map of the world different from a globe?

globe
(glōb)
a ball-shaped object that has all of the earth's areas of land and bodies of water drawn on it

continent
(kŏn'tə-nənt)
one of the earth's seven great areas of land

border
(bôr'dər)
the line where one area ends and another begins

Looking at North America

The United States is on the continent of North America. Its neighbors are Canada and Mexico. Part of the **border** between the United States and Canada follows the Great Lakes. Part of the border between the United States and Mexico follows a river, the Rio Grande. The United States, Canada, and Mexico are the largest countries in North America. South of Mexico is an area called Central America. It includes several smaller countries. East of Mexico is a group of island countries called the West Indies. Northeast of Canada is the country of Greenland.

[?] Which are the three largest countries on the continent of North America?

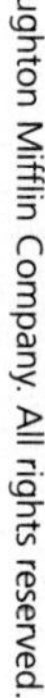

Summary continues on next page

Looking at California

California is a state in the United States. Three other states share a border with California. They are Oregon, Nevada, and Arizona. California's western border is the Pacific Ocean. The southern edge of California borders Mexico.

[?] Name the states, country, and body of water on California's borders.

Zooming in on California

Imagine you are on the space shuttle. You fly across the Pacific Ocean toward the California coast. You pass over Monterey Bay. Then you continue southeast, flying over the farmlands and rivers of the Central Valley. As you leave the valley, you fly over mountains to the desert. There you and the shuttle land.

[?] What geographic features of California does the space shuttle pass over as it is landing?

Name: Date:

CHAPTER 1

Lesson 2 Preview

California's Regions

(*Oh, California* pp. 12–18)

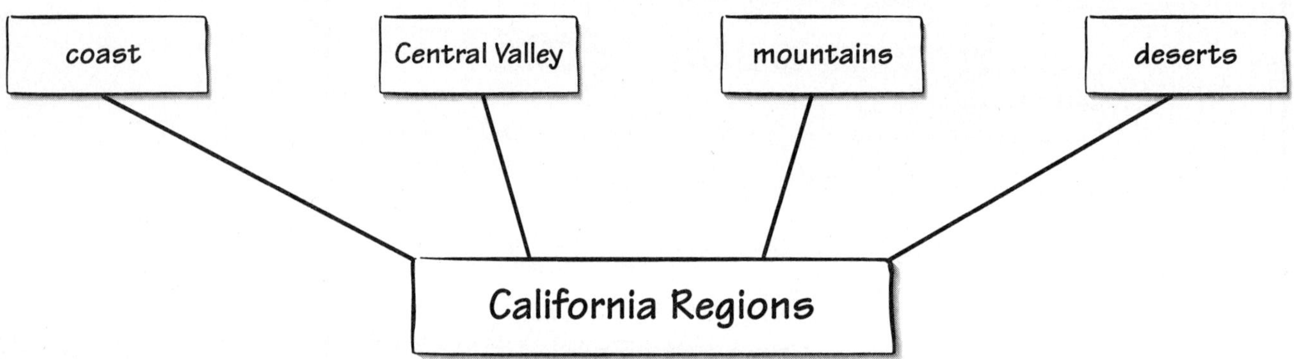

1. Look at the graphic organizer above. Then write the word that best completes these sentences.

a. The state of California can be divided into ______________ main regions.

b. California's regions are named for ______________ features.

2. Look at the map on page 13 of your text. Which of California's regions is entirely surrounded by other regions?

____

Name: Date:

CHAPTER 1

Lesson 2 Reading Strategy

California's Regions

(*Oh, California* pp. 12–18)

Summarize This reading strategy helps you remember key points about what you have read. When you get to a good break in your reading, stop and write down the main ideas of what you have read.

1. **Read the "Four Regions" section on page 13. Check the best summary about California's regions for this section.**

    ___ The geography of California is more varied than most other states.

    ___ Scientists can't figure out California's geography.

    ___ The geography of California is the same across the state.

2. **Read "The Coast" on page 14. Check the best summary.**

    ___ Most people live on the southern coast near Los Angeles.

    ___ The northern coast is closer to Oregon than the southern coast.

    ___ The northern coast is cool and damp with many forests, while the southern coast region is warmer and drier.

3. **Read the section "The Central Valley" on page 15. Write a short summary of the section to tell about California's Central Valley region.**

    ____

    ____

4. **Read the sections "The Mountains" on page 16 and "The Deserts" on page 17. Complete the chart to summarize how these regions differ.**

	The Mountains	The Deserts
Geography/climate		
Animals/plants		

CHAPTER 1

Lesson 2 Summary

California's Regions

Summary also on Audiotape

(*Oh, California* pp. 12–18)

Thinking Focus: How are California's geographic regions different from one another?

Four Regions

California's **geography** can be divided into four main **regions:**

- The coast
- The Central Valley
- The mountains
- The desert

Each region of California held different challenges for early settlers. The first Europeans came to California by sea and braved the storms along the coast. Later, settlers from the east had to cross high mountain ranges and hot deserts. Still later, the farmers of the Central Valley had to find ways to bring water to their crops. Each region also had many advantages. Features such as natural beauty, rich soil, and good weather brought different people to different areas of the state.

geography
(jē-ŏg′rə-fē)
the land and water features that are found in an area

region
(rē′jən)
an area of land whose features set it off from other areas

[?] Name four geographic regions of California and give one word to describe each region.

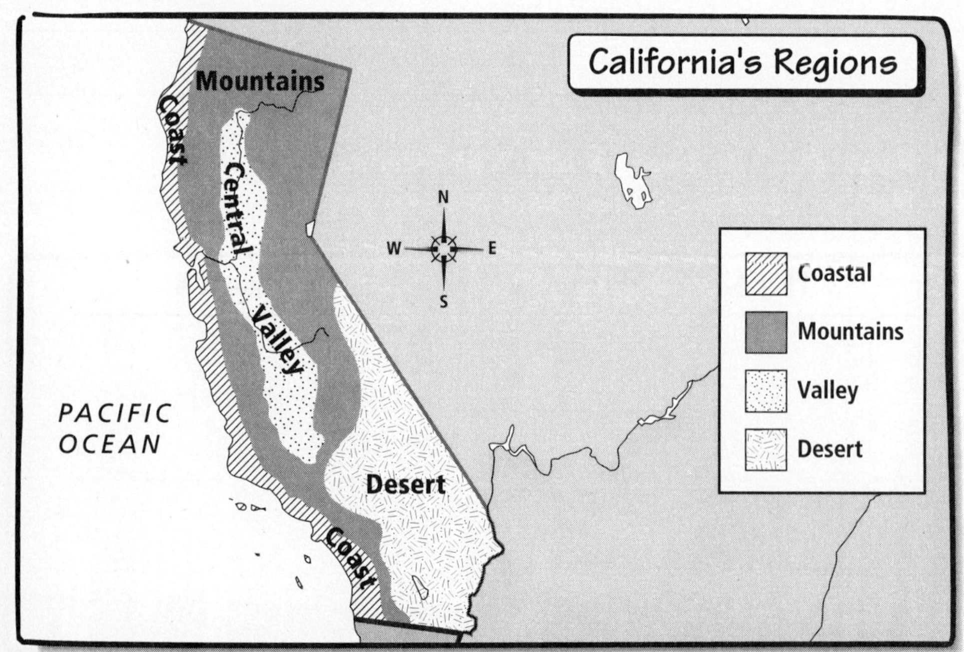

Summary continues on next page

The Coast

The northern coast of California is cool, damp, and foggy. This wet **climate** helps the thick forests grow. The climate along the southern coast is much drier. Cities there have sunny weather with little rain.

[?] How is the northern coast of California different from the southern coast?

climate
(klī′mĭt)
the usual type of weather in an area

mountain range
(mōun′tən rānj)
a long row of mountains

The Central Valley

The Central Valley has some of the best farmland in the world. Its winter rains, summer heat, and rich soil make the area perfect for raising crops and animals.

[?] Why is the Central Valley such a good farming area?

The Mountains

People camp, hike, ski, and enjoy nature in California's mountains. One **mountain range**, the Sierra Nevada, has three national parks to protect its beauty. Melting winter snow from the Sierra Nevada supplies water to farms and cities. On the forest slopes, lumbering is a major industry.

[?] Why do you think California's mountain region attracts visitors from all over the world?

The Deserts

The Mojave Desert and the Colorado Desert make up most of California's desert region. Temperatures are very hot in the day and very cold at night. There is little rain. In order to survive, cactus plants store water in their thick skins. Animals get water by eating desert plants. The Fort Mojave Indians have lived in the Mojave Desert for thousands of years.

[?] How are desert plants and animals well-suited to their climates?

Name: Date:

CHAPTER 1

Lesson 3 Preview

California's Resources

(*Oh, California* pp. 21–25)

Natural and Human Resources

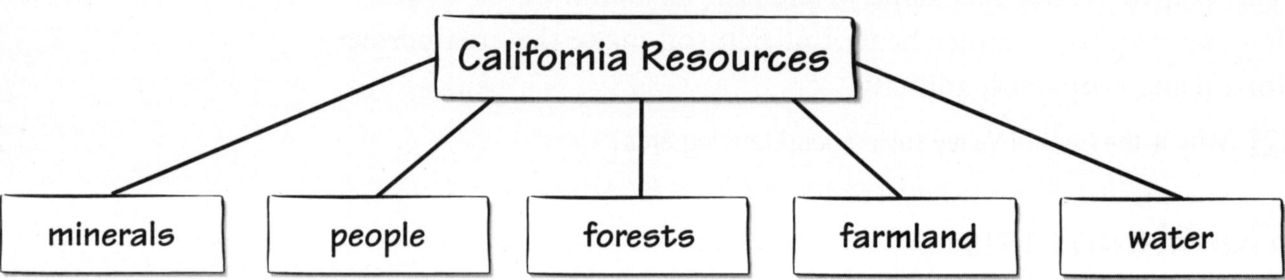

1. **Look at the graphic organizer above. Then check all the statements below that best describe California's resources.**

   ___ Forests and farmland are examples of water resources.

   ___ Forests, farmland, and people need water resources to live.

   ___ People use their skills and talents to make a living in California.

   ___ Most of California's resources come from the desert.

2. **Look at the map on page 22 of your text. What natural resources are shown on this map and in which geographic regions are they located?**

Name: Date:

CHAPTER 1

Lesson 3 Reading Strategy

California's Resources

(*Oh, California* pp. 21–25)

Using the Visuals This reading strategy helps you to use photographs, maps, charts, and illustrations to understand what you read. As you read, be sure to study the visuals and carefully read the captions.

1. **Look at the map and the photograph on page 21. Read the caption. What do you think the yellow areas on the map show? Circle the best answer.**
   a. The yellow areas all belong to California.
   b. The yellow areas show other places that have volcanoes.
   c. The yellow areas all exploded on June 14, 1914.

2. **Look at the photograph on page 22 and read the caption. What can you learn from this picture? Circle the best answer.**
   a. The copper used to make pipes comes from a rock in the ground.
   b. Metals are prettier when they're refined and polished.
   c. California imports a lot of pipe from other states.

3. **Look at the map on page 22 and read the key. What can you learn from this picture? Circle the best answer.**
   a. Most farmland is not in the Central Valley.
   b. Forests are found mostly in the northern part of the state.
   c. Mining takes place mostly along the coast.

4. **Look at the pictures at the bottom of page 23 and the top of page 25. Read the captions. What can you learn from these pictures?**

____

____

5. **Imagine you are adding symbols to the map key on page 22. Draw the symbols you would use to show people and water.**

People	Water

CHAPTER 1

Summary also on Audiotape

Lesson 3 Summary
California's Resources

(*Oh, California* pp. 21–25)

Thinking Focus: What natural resources are found in California?

Mining California's Resources

Millions of years ago, much of California was under water. Huge forces within the earth, like volcanoes and earthquakes, pushed the land above the ocean. These same forces created the many kinds of **minerals** that are found in California. These minerals are some of California's many **natural resources.** The people who live in California make up the state's **human resources.**

? How did changes in the land help to create California's natural resources?

mineral
(mĭn'ər-əl)
a natural substance, such as gold or copper, often found by digging in the ground

natural resource
(năch'ər-əl rē'sôrs')
a material found in nature that can be used by people

human resource
(hyōō'mən rē'sôrs')
a person who can do a job or a service

California's Natural Resources

Forests provide natural beauty and homes for wildlife.

Rich soil helps farmers grow many fruits, vegetables and cotton.

California's minerals include oil, gold, copper, and iron.

Water is one of California's most valuable resources.

Summary continues on next page

Caring for California's Resources

California's trees are an important natural resource. Its forests provide homes for birds and animals. The wood from the trees is a natural resource used to make homes, paper, and many other things.

Some forests are left alone so people in the future will have the wood they need. Still others are left alone for their beauty. California's sequoia trees are a good example. These trees are the largest and one of the oldest trees on Earth. They can live for thousands of years. People come from all over the world to see these trees.

California's farmland is another important natural resource. Most of the farmland is in the Central Valley and the Imperial Valley. Forests, farmland, and people all use water—one of California's most important natural resources. But California does not have much water. The people of California must take care to use the water wisely to keep it clean and plentiful.

[?] Why are trees a resource to be used and protected?

Chapter Overview
The First Californians

Fill in the black spaces below with information from the chapter.

When:
14,000 years ago–1769
Where:
West coast of North America
Who:
Native Americans

The First Californians

The First Californians

Archaeologists look for

____

Early people live in

____

California Indians Use Regional Resources

People from the North Coast

- food
- trade items
- _______________

People from the Mountains

- _______________
- _______________
- ceremonies

People from the South Coast

- food
- _______________
- clothing

People of the Deserts

- food
- _______________
- _______________
- _______________

People of the Valley

- _______________
- _______________
- _______________
- ceremonies

Name: Date:

CHAPTER 2

Lesson 1 Preview

Discovering the First Californians

(*Oh, California* pp. 32–36)

Migration to California
Initial Event
Ice Age Land Bridge
Event 2
Hunters arrive in California.
Final Outcome
100 tribes live in California.

1. The graphic overview above shows three time periods in the history of California. Read the word groups below. Use the graphic overview to help you decide the correct order of the word groups. Then circle the letter of the correct word group.

a. hunters arrive, people cross land bridge, people live in tribes
b. people live in tribes, people cross land bridge, hunters arrive
c. people cross land bridge, hunters arrive, people live in tribes
d. hunters arrive, people live in tribes, people cross land bridge

2. Look at the map on page 33. Scientists believe that people first came to North America from Asia. Write sentences that describe the routes that people took when they settled in North America.

Name: Date:

C H A P T E R 2

Lesson 1 Reading Strategy

Discovering the First Californians

(*Oh, California* pp. 32–36)

Evaluate This reading strategy helps you recognize the difference between facts and opinions. A fact is something that can be proven to be true. An opinion is a belief based on what a person thinks or feels.

1. **Read the section "The First Californians" on page 33. Circle the statement below that is a fact.**
   a. People have lived in California for millions of years.
   b. Some people think animals swam across the Bering Strait.
   c. Today, Asia and North America are separated by the Bering Strait.

2. **Read the section "Scientists Find Clues to Early Life" on page 34. Circle the statement below that is not a fact.**
   a. Archaeologists search for objects made and used by people who lived long ago.
   b. Archaeologists always understand the clues they find.
   c. Archaeologists know that post holes show were homes once stood.

3. **Write a sentence from page 35 that states a fact.**

____

____

4. **Read the section "People Live in Tribes" on pages 35 and 36. Write two facts and two opinions about this section.**

Facts	Opinions
1.	1.
2.	2.

CHAPTER 2

Lesson 1 Summary

Discovering the First Californians

(*Oh, California* pp. 32–36)

Summary also on Audiotape

Thinking Focus: How do archaeologists know about the first people who came to California?

The First Californians

Native Indian groups living in California today believe that their people have always lived there. But many scientists believe that the first people arrived in what is now California about 12,000 years ago. These people may have been the later relatives of ancient hunters. These hunters had crossed a grassy plain from Asia to North America. You could not make this trip by land today. A body of water called the Bering **Strait** now separates Asia and North America.

strait
(strāt)
a narrow passage of water that connects two larger bodies of water

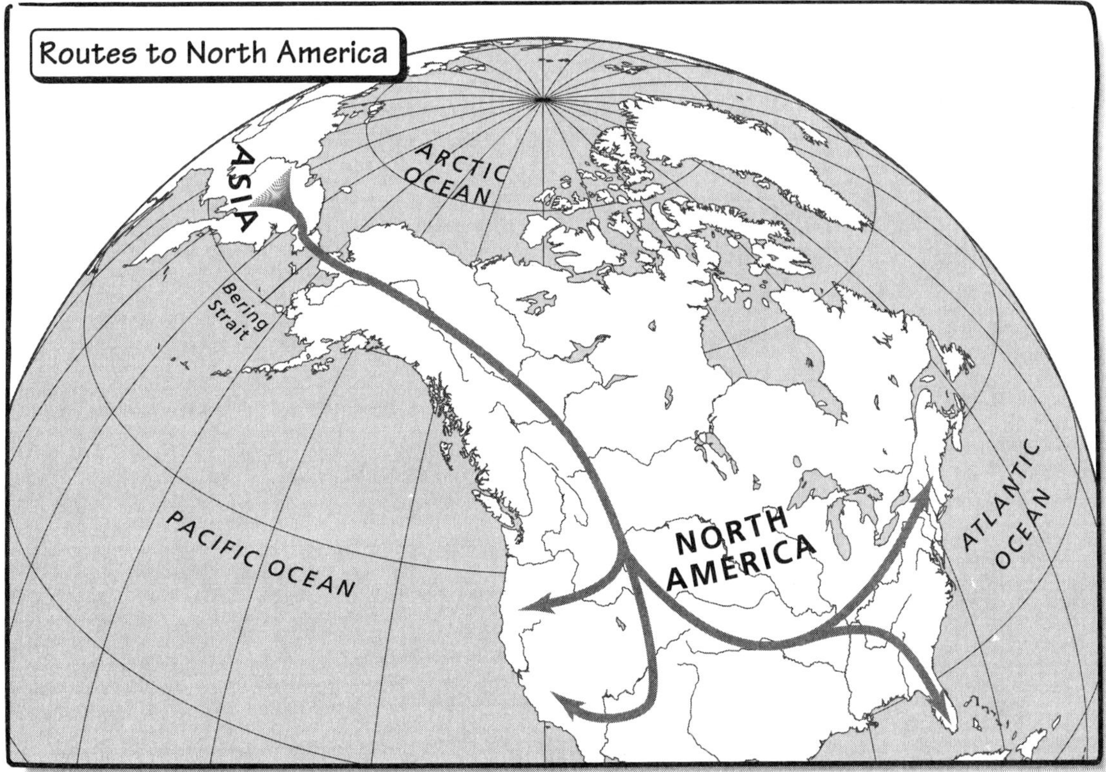

? What are the different ideas about how the first people came to California?

Scientists Find Clues to Early Life

Scientists called **archaeologists** try to decide how objects from long ago were used. For example, a stone with a chipped edge may have been used to cut meat or to scrape animal skins.

In 1970, an archaeologist named Stuart Streuver found large, round marks on the ground in Illinois. The marks showed where wooden posts had held up the walls of an Indian home. Streuver had found the first permanent homes in North America. Some findings puzzle archaeologists. More clues are needed before some mysteries can be explained.

archaeologist
(är′kē-ŏl′ə-jĭst)
a scientist who looks for clues about how people once lived

tribe
(trīb)
a group of people who live in the same area and are related to each other

[?] Find examples in the text that show the way archaeologists use objects from the past to understand how people lived long ago.

People Live in Tribes

The first people in California lived in villages along the coast or by rivers and streams. As the villages grew, some people moved away to start new villages. Men and women often married people who lived in nearby villages and were part of the same **tribe**. These people shared the same language, customs, and beliefs.

The word "tribe" is not always the best word to describe California's American Indians. Sometimes one tribe name has been given to several different peoples. All American Indians belong to two groups—their tribal nation and the United States.

The first European explorers in the Americas believed they were in India. They called the people they saw Indians. Today these people are known as American Indians or Native Americans.

[?] What is a tribe?

Name: Date:

CHAPTER 2

Lesson 2 Preview

Living on the Rivers and Coasts

(*Oh, California* pp. 37–41)

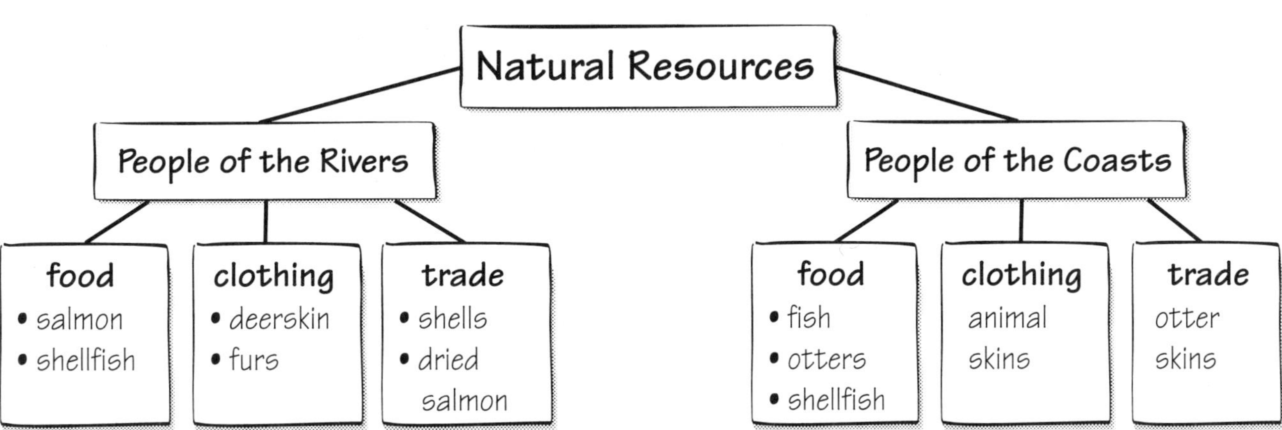

1. Look at the graphic overview above. Then write the words that best complete this sentence.

Both the people of the rivers and the people of the coasts ate

________________ and ________________.

2. Look at the photographs on page 39 and read the captions. Write two sentences to tell how California Indians used dentalium shells and redwood trees.

____

____

Name: ______________________ Date: ______________________

CHAPTER 2

Lesson 2 Reading Strategy

Living on the Rivers and Coasts

(*Oh, California* pp. 37–41)

Compare and Contrast This reading strategy helps you understand how events are similar and different. As you read about historical events, think about how they compare and contrast with events you already know.

1. **Read the section "People from the North" on pages 38 and 39 about how the Yurok lived long ago. Fill in the chart below with information describing the food and clothing of these Yurok.**

Food	Clothing

2. **Read the section "People from the South" on pages 40 and 41 about how the Chumash lived long ago. Fill in the chart below with information describing the food and clothing of these Chumash.**

Food	Clothing

3. **Name one way in which the food of the Yurok and the Chumash was similar.**

____

Name one way in which the food was different.

____

4. **What special resource did the Chumash have that the Yurok did not?**

____

CHAPTER 2

Summary also on Audiotape

Lesson 2 Summary

Living on the Rivers and Coasts

(*Oh, California* pp. 37–41)

Thinking Focus: How did Indians of the rivers and coasts use the natural resources around them?

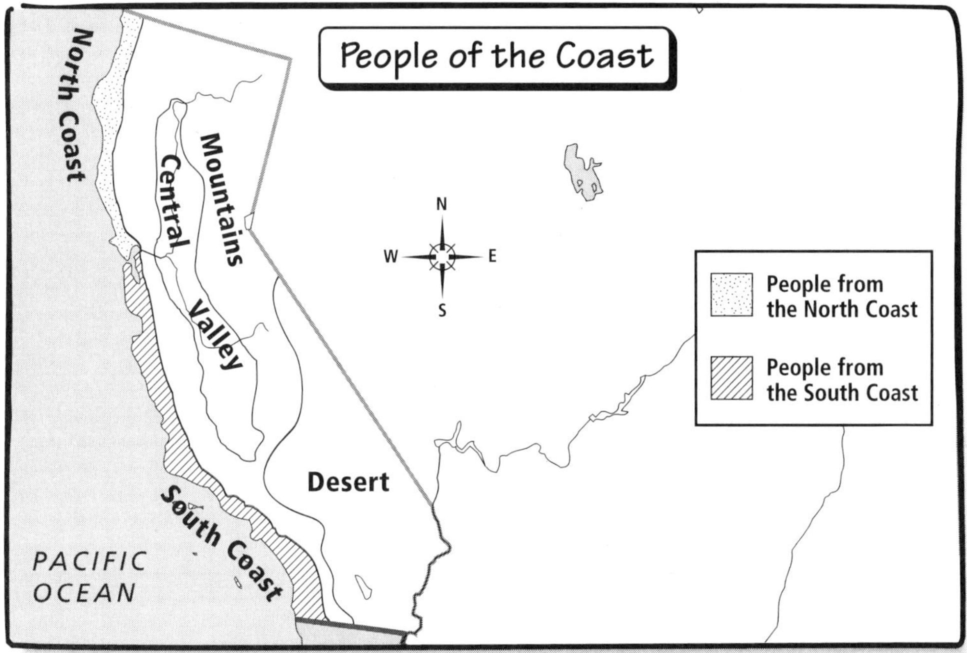

People from the North

The people of the north tell a **creation story** of how the rivers and oceans came to be. The story is important because much of their food and wealth came from the rivers and ocean.

The northern Pacific coast and the northwestern mountains were home to the Yurok and their neighbors the Hupa and the Karok. This region provided rich natural resources. The men wore deerskin clothing and used redwood trees to build houses and make canoes. The women wore apron skirts of deerskin or fur.

Along the coast, the people ate mussels, oysters, and clams. In the mountains, they caught salmon. Each spring, the Yurok

creation story
(krē-ā′shən stôr′ē)
a story handed down from adults to children that explains the beliefs of a people and the way they view the world.

Summary continues on next page

placed woven stick fences across the Klamath River to stop the salmon as they swam upstream. Then the men speared the fish.

The Yurok traveled along the coast to **trade** their salmon for dentalium shells. These shells were hard to find, and the Yurok used these shells as money. The Yurok traded the beads for tools or soapstone bowls. These were things they could not make from the resources in their region.

trade
(trād)
to give something to another person in return for something of theirs

community
(kə-myo͞o′nĭ-tē)
a group of people living together under the same leader

[?] What were the important natural resources for the Yurok?

People from the South

The Chumash built their villages along the Pacific coast where California curves inward near Santa Barbara. They used clams, crabs, and sea otters for food, clothing, and trade.

The Chumash had one special resource. This resource was tar. The Chumash used a kind of tar called asphaltum, mixed with pine pitch, to waterproof their baskets and to seal the cracks between the boards of their large wooden canoes.

The Chumash were well-known boat builders. Their tomols, or canoes, were made from pieces of redwood that had washed up on the shore.

Some Chumash villages were small. Others were as large as a thousand people. Each large village had a leader, or chief. Several small villages sometimes chose one chief to serve all of them together. The chief watched over everything that went on in the **community.**

Being chief was usually a job that was handed down from father to son. But if a chief had no sons, a daughter might serve as the next leader.

[?] How did the Chumash use the natural resources where they lived?

Name: Date:

CHAPTER 2

Lesson 3 Preview

Life at Inland Villages

(*Oh, California* pp. 43–49)

Life at Indian Villages

Tribe	Daily Activities	Traditions
Miwok	fishing, making tools, gathering berries, nuts, and plants, weaving baskets	religious ceremonies in sweathouse acorn dance/songs
Maidu	hunted small animals preserved food	religious ceremonies bear dance
Mojave	farming trade	religious ceremonies rain dance

1. **Look at the graphic overview above. Then answer this question: Which tradition did all these Indian groups have in common?**

   ____

2. **Look at the picture of the Miwok village on page 44. What work do you see the people of this village performing?**

   ____

   ____

Name: Date:

CHAPTER 2

Lesson 3 Reading Strategy

Life at Inland Villages

(*Oh, California* pp. 44–49)

Finding the Main Idea This reading strategy helps you organize and remember what you read. When you finish a selection, jot down the main idea and its supporting details.

1. **Read the section "People of the Valleys" on pages 44 and 45. Write *M* next to the sentence that best tells the main idea of the selection.**

   ___ Members of the Miwok village had special jobs to do.

   ___ Miwok children learned skills by playing games.

   ___ Miwok men fished and hunted and made basket fish traps, bows, and arrows.

2. **Read the section "People of the Mountains" on page 47. Write a sentence that best tells the main idea of the selection.**

   ____

3. **Which sentences on page 47 give supporting details to the main idea: Ceremonies were an important part of Maidu life.**

   ____

   ____

4. **Read the section "People of the Desert" on pages 48 and 49. Then complete the chart below by listing at least three supporting details.**

Main Idea	Supporting Details
The Mojave learned to use the resources in the desert to meet their needs.	1.
	2.
	3.

Summary also on Audiotape

CHAPTER 2

Lesson 3 Summary

Life at Inland Villages

(*Oh, California* pp. 43–49)

Thinking Focus: What did children learn from adults in Indian communities?

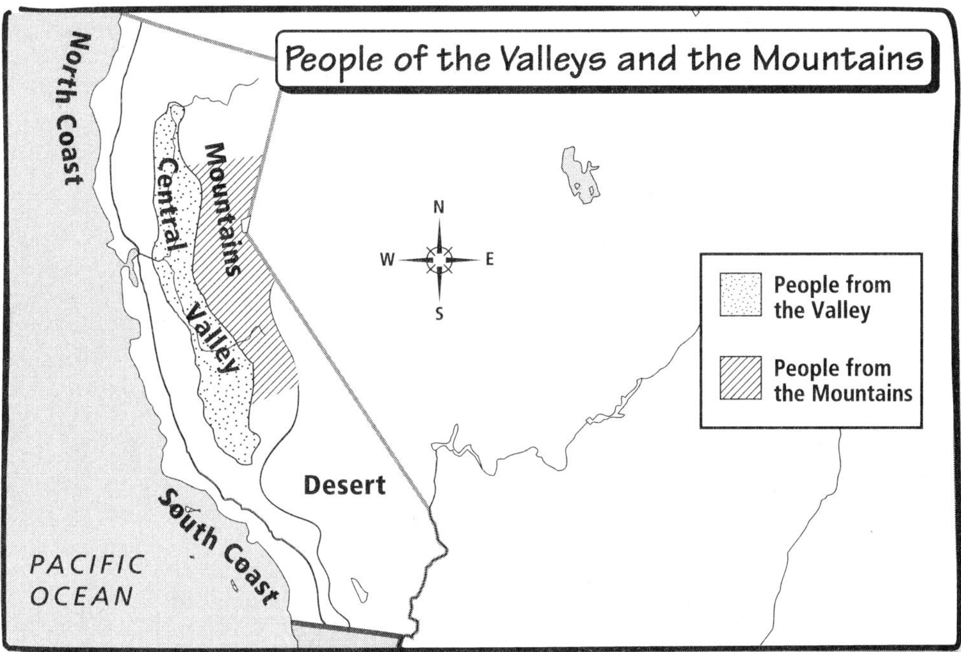

People of the Valleys

The Miwok lived in the Central Valley. They used the valley's resources to meet their needs. Gualacomne was a Miwok community on the banks of the Sacramento River. Almost 200 people lived here in earthen homes. Miwok boys learned to do special jobs by watching the men. They learned to:

- make arrow points
- make basket fish traps
- spear fish
- make bows and arrows

Miwok girls learned from their mothers how to

- gather berries, nuts, and plants
- make flour from acorns
- weave baskets

? How would Chumash village activities differ from those of the Miwok?

Summary continues on next page

People of the Mountains

The Maidu lived in the mountain valleys of the Sierra Nevada. This region had many plants and animals that were used for food.

Winters in the mountains are cold and long. So the Maidu had to preserve and store food for the months when animals were hard to hunt. Dried berries, greens, and deer meat helped villagers survive the long winter.

When spring came, the people celebrated. They invited neighboring villagers for a special **ceremony**—a bear dance. The Maidu believe the bear is a spirit and has powers greater than people. In the fall the Maidu celebrated the acorn harvest. During these gatherings, children learned the **traditions** of their community.

ceremony
(sĕr′ə-mō′nē)
a planned event that marked a special occasion

tradition
(trə-dĭsh′ən)
a way of doing things that is handed down by older people to younger ones

[?] How do the traditions and ceremonies of the Indians show their closeness to the natural world?

People of the Desert

The Mojave Desert lies in southeastern California. In the desert, days are very hot and nights are very cold. There is little rain. Still, plants and animals learned to live in the desert. The Mojave, Chemehuevis, and other tribes of southern California also learned to live there. They hunted deer and bighorn sheep. They gathered seeds and fruit from cactus plants and trees.

The Colorado River was an important resource. Each spring the river flooded, leaving a fine layer of mud on the land. The Mojave grew squash, melons, corn, and pumpkins in this rich soil. The Mojave fished from the river and hunted on its banks. They traded for things they could not make from desert resources. These items included wooden bowls, horn spoons, and shell beads.

[?] How did the Mojave differ from other California tribes?

Chapter Overview
Spanish Explorers and Settlers

Fill in the blank spaces below with information from the chapter.

When:
1519-1832

Where:
Alta California

Who:
Spanish Explorers and Settlers

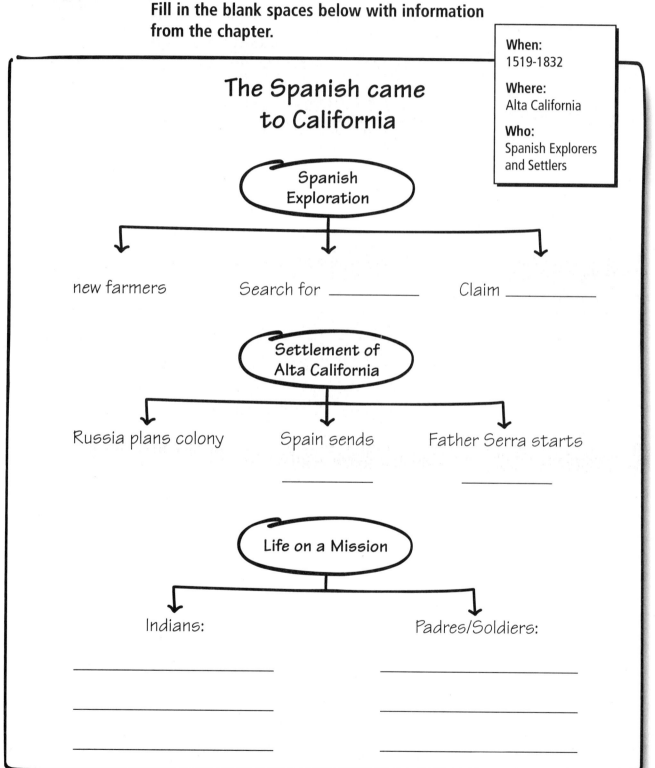

The Spanish came to California

Spanish Exploration

- new farmers
- Search for ___________
- Claim ___________

Settlement of Alta California

- Russia plans colony
- Spain sends ___________
- Father Serra starts ___________

Life on a Mission

Indians:

____
____
____

Padres/Soldiers:

____
____
____

Name: Date:

CHAPTER 3

Lesson 1 Preview

Early Explorers

(*Oh, California* pp. 58–62)

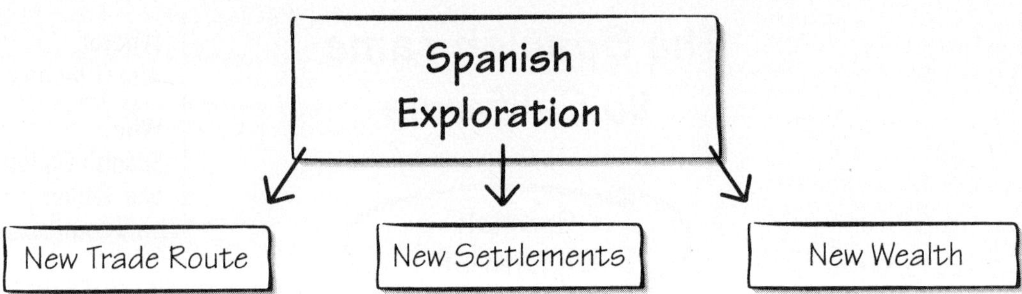

1. **Look at the graphic overview above. Use the following words to fill in the blanks below.**

trade route	wealth	settlements

   a. Spanish explorers first came to California looking for a ____________________ to India.

   b. They hoped that finding a shorter way to India would bring them great ____________________.

   c. Later, priests and colonists started ____________________ in California.

2. **Look at the map on page 59 of your text. It shows the land in the Americas that Spain claimed in the 1550s. Write a sentence that describes the location of the lands claimed by Spain.**

____

____

____

____

____

____

____

Name: Date:

CHAPTER 3

Lesson 1 Reading Strategy

Early Explorers

(*Oh, California* pp. 58–62)

Self-Question This reading strategy helps you stay focused on what you read. Ask yourself questions before you read a section. Then read to see if you can find the answer to your questions.

1. **Read the heading "Spain Starts a New Settlement" on page 59. Check the question you think this section will answer.**

   ___ Where did Spain start a new settlement?

   ___ What did English captains do to Spanish ships?

   ___ Where in North America is California?

   Read to the bottom of page 59 to see if that question was answered.

2. **Read the heading "Cabrillo Explores the Coast" on page 60. Write a question you think this section will answer.**

   ____

   Read the section to see if the question you chose was answered.

3. **Read "Galleons Sail for Riches" and "Drake Threatens New Spain" on pages 60 and 62. In the chart, write questions you think the sections will answer. Then read the sections and write any answers you find.**

My Questions	What I Learned by Reading
1.	1.
2.	2.

C H A P T E R 3

Lesson 1 Summary

Early Explorers

(*Oh, California* pp. 58–62)

Thinking Focus: Why did Spain want to explore the California coast?

Spain Starts a New Settlement

After Columbus reached the West Indies in 1492, other Spanish explorers led **expeditions** in the Americas. In 1519, Hernán Cortés and his men sailed west from Cuba to Mexico. They were looking for silver, gold, and other riches. In Mexico, they found Aztec cities with silver and gold treasures. The Spanish government began a **colony** in Mexico called New Spain. The explorers forced the Aztecs to work for them. All the riches they found were sent back to Spain.

expedition
(ĕk'spĭ-dĭsh'ən)
a journey planned by a group of people for a certain reason

colony
(kŏl'ə-nē)
a land controlled by another country

In 1542, Juan Rodríguez Cabrillo set sail from the west coast of New Spain. He was looking for a waterway that connected the Pacific and Atlantic oceans. Cabrillo found harbors at what is now San Diego and San Francisco. Cabrillo and his men never found a water route. But they were the first Europeans to visit California.

About 20 years after Cabrillo's expedition, traders began sailing from New Spain across the Pacific ocean to Asia. They reached the Philippine Islands in ships called galleons. On the return trip, winds carried the galleons to California. From there, the galleons sailed south to get back to New Spain.

? Why did Spanish explorers first come to North and South America?

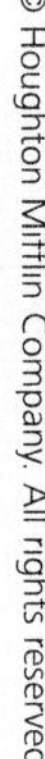

Summary continues on next page

Drake Threatens New Spain

After 1570, Queen Elizabeth I of England became interested in the treasures found in New Spain. She sent Francis Drake to the Americas. Drake attacked Spanish ships in the Caribbean and stole their gold and silver. He also attacked Spanish colonies along the Pacific coast.

The queen was pleased with the riches Drake brought back. She sent him on a round-the-world trip to explore new sea routes. Drake sailed around South America and up the west coast. In 1579, he found a harbor in northern California and claimed it for England. Then he sailed across the Pacific.

Drake's voyage placed Spanish rule in the Pacific Ocean in danger. The Spanish learned that they needed settlements in California to protect their colonies from attack.

[?] Why did Spain feel threatened by Francis Drake?

Name: Date:

CHAPTER 3

Lesson 2 Preview

First European Settlers

(*Oh, California* pp. 65–69)

1. **Look at the graphic overview above. Then answer the following question: What caused Spain to settle Alta California?**

2. **Look at the photograph on page 69 of your text. Then look at the map on page 68. Which explorer took a route to Alta California that went through the type of area shown in the photograph?**

Name: Date:

CHAPTER 3

Lesson 2 Reading Strategy

First European Settlers

(*Oh, California* pp. 65–69)

Predict/Infer This reading strategy helps you understand what you have read and what you will read next. Before you read a section, think about the titles, pictures, and captions. Then think about what will happen in the selection.

1. Read the lesson title on page 65 and the opening paragraphs. Then look at the picture and read the caption. What do you predict will be the main event described in this lesson? Check your answer.

___ How the Spanish settled California.

___ Why soldiers were needed on the expeditions.

2. Write two clues from the text that helped you make your prediction.

____

3. Read the text under the heading "Spain Rediscovers Alta California" on page 65 up to the diary entry on page 67. What do you predict will happen on the sea and land expeditions? Check your answer.

___ Spain will decide not to start new settlements in Alta California.

___ Both the sea and land expeditions will face long, hard journeys.

___ The sea expedition will have an easier journey than the land expeditions.

4. Look at the map on page 68 and read the first paragraph under "Anza Takes Another Route." Then fill in the chart below.

What I Know	What I Predict

CHAPTER 3

Lesson 2 Summary

First European Settlers

(*Oh, California* pp. 65–69)

Summary also on Audiotape

Thinking Focus: Why did Spain want to settle Alta California?

Spain Rediscovers Alta California

For over 200 years, Spain had little interest in California. Then, in 1768, Spain learned that Russia wanted to start a colony in California. Spain quickly began to settle the land it had claimed.

Don José de Galvez, an official from New Spain, wanted to set up forts and **missions** in California's upper region, called Alta California. Galvez hoped that setting up forts and missions would keep Russia from claiming the land. Priests had already set up missions on Baja California, the lower **peninsula** of California.

In 1769, three expeditions left Baja for San Diego. One went by sea, two went by land. The governor of New Spain, Gaspar de Portolá, led one land expedition. A priest named Father Junípero Serra went with him. They had to cross deserts and mountains. Several men died along the way. The sea route was no easier. The ships were in danger of hitting rocks. One ship sank with all its men. It took many months for the expeditions to reach San Diego.

Portolá moved on from San Diego searching for a good harbor. He found Monterey Bay the following year.

[?] Why was the Portolá expedition important to Spain and the Catholic Church?

mission
(mĭsh'ən)
a settlement where Catholic priests teach their religious beliefs to the people nearby

peninsula
(pə-nĭn'syə-lə)
a finger of land that has water on three sides

Summary continues on next page

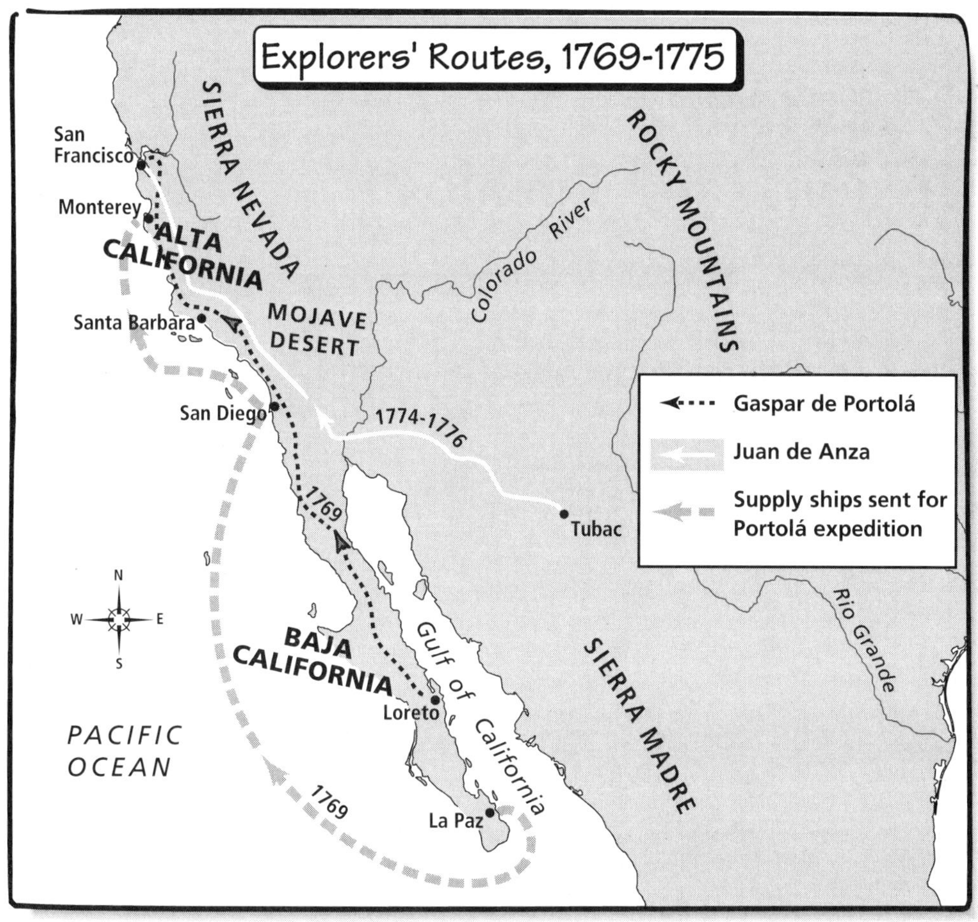

Anza Takes Another Route

A Spanish soldier named Juan Bautista de Anza wanted to find an easier route to Alta California. He set out from the Sonora desert in present-day Arizona. Anza took 30 families with him, promising them free land. They reached Monterey in March 1776. Anza's route was just as hard as the Baja routes. The deserts and mountains of southern California were hard to cross. Deserts and mountains kept Alta California set apart from New Spain for many years.

[?] Why did people decide to take the long journey with Captain Anza?

Name: Date:

CHAPTER 3

Lesson 3 Preview

Presidios, Missions, and Pueblos

(*Oh, California* pp. 71–74)

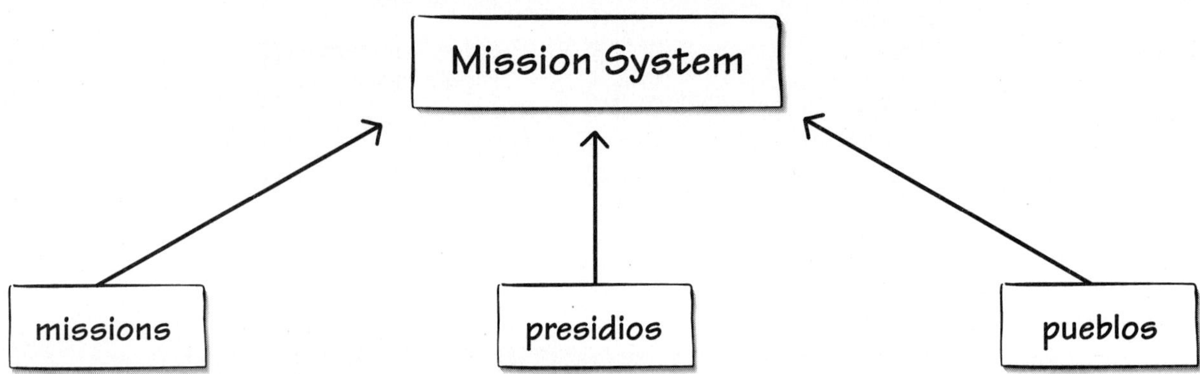

1. **Look at the graphic overview above.**

   The mission system that the Spanish built to settle Alta California was made up of missions, ______________, and ______________.

2. **Look at the map on page 74 of your text. Then read the question below. Circle the letter of the best answer and write your reasons for choosing that answer on the lines below.**

   Where in California were the missions and presidios built?

   a. in the mountains

   b. in the Central Valley

   c. along the coast

   d. in the desert

   ____

   ____

   ____

   ____

   ____

Name: Date:

CHAPTER 3

Lesson 3 Reading Strategy

Presidios, Missions, and Pueblos

(*Oh, California* pp. 71–74)

Summarize This reading strategy helps you remember key points about what you have read. When you get to a good break in your reading, stop and write down the main ideas of what you have read.

1. **Read the first paragraph under the heading "Father Serra Starts the Mission Chain" on page 72. Check the best summary for this paragraph.**
   ___ Father Serra was a good businessman.
   ___ Father Serra was a very religious man.
   ___ Father Serra always wanted to be a soldier.

2. **Read the section "The Work Begins" on pages 72–73. Write a sentence that best summarizes this section.**

   ____

   ____

3. **Read the section "More Missions to Build" on page 73. Write a short summary of Father Serra's work building missions.**

   ____

4. **Read the section "El Camino Real Connects the Missions" on pages 73–74. Complete the chart to summarize the relationships among the missions, presidios, and pueblos along El Camino Real.**

	Food	Protection	Work
Missions			
Presidios			
Pueblos			

CHAPTER 3

Summary also on Audiotape

Lesson 3 Summary

Presidios, Missions, and Pueblos

(*Oh, California* pp. 71–74)

Thinking Focus: How did the missions, presidios, and pueblos help each other?

Father Serra Starts the Mission Chain

Father Serra thought he could help the Indians by converting them to Christianity. But the Indians already had their own religious beliefs. In order to bring the Indians to the missions, Father Serra gave them food, clothing, and iron pots. Then the **padres** tried to teach them Christian traditions. The padres also put the Indians to work building churches and planting crops. Father Serra started nine missions in all. Indian workers helped the missions grow.

Building forts and towns was part of Spain's plan for settling Alta California. Spanish forts were called **presidios.** They protected the missions. Towns, called **pueblos**, were also started near the missions for settlers from Mexico.

[?] What did Father Serra have to do when he started a new mission?

padre
(pä'drā)
a priest

presidio
(prĭ-sē'dē-ō')
a fort that protected a mission

pueblo
(pwĕb'lō)
a town built near a mission

Summary continues on next page

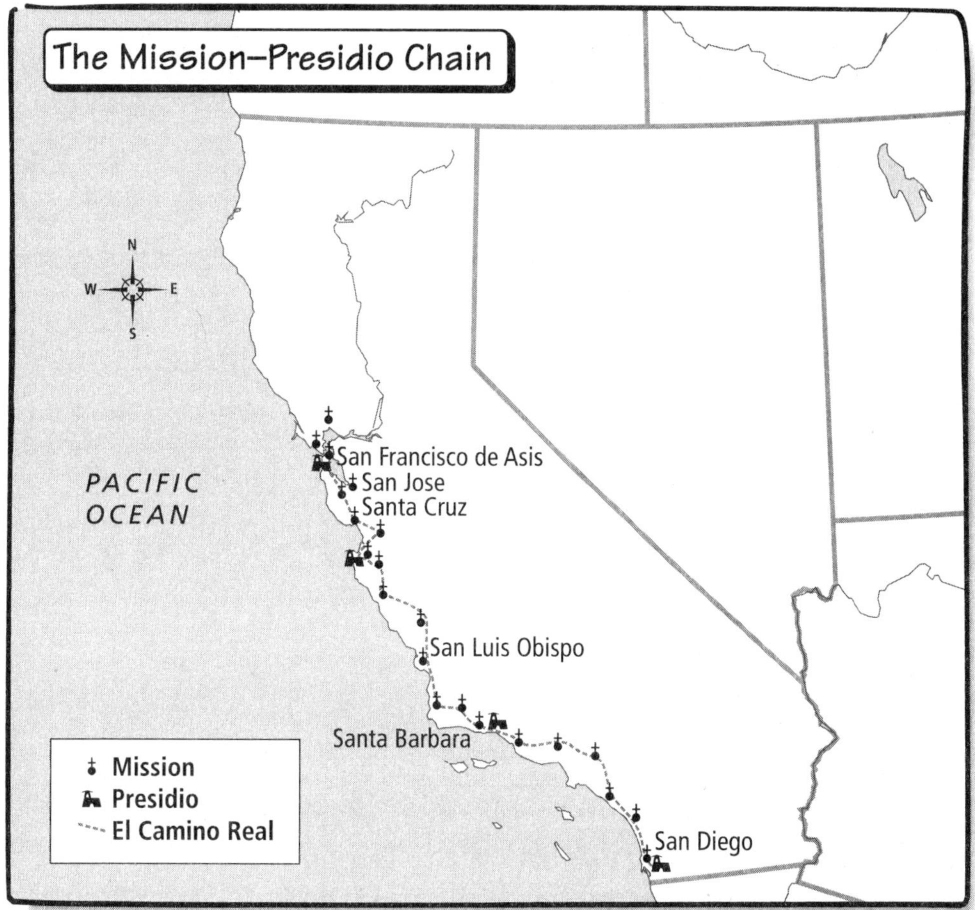

El Camino Real Connects the Missions

The Spanish built many missions along the California coast. They were all connected by a road called El Camino Real. People traveling along the road could spend each night of their journey at a mission.

Many of the missions looked like small villages. They had orchards and vineyards, workshops, and a church. Some missions had presidios to protect them. A presidio was like a village, too. It had houses inside the large earthen walls. Soldiers and their families lived in the presidios.

The pueblo of Los Angeles was settled by 12 Mexican families. The Spanish government gave each family two lots of land to settle there. Families lived on one lot and planted a garden on the other. In return, the families gave some of their crops to the presidios.

[?] What was the purpose of El Camino Real?

Name: Date:

CHAPTER 3

Lesson 4 Preview

Life on a Mission

(*Oh, California* pp. 75–79)

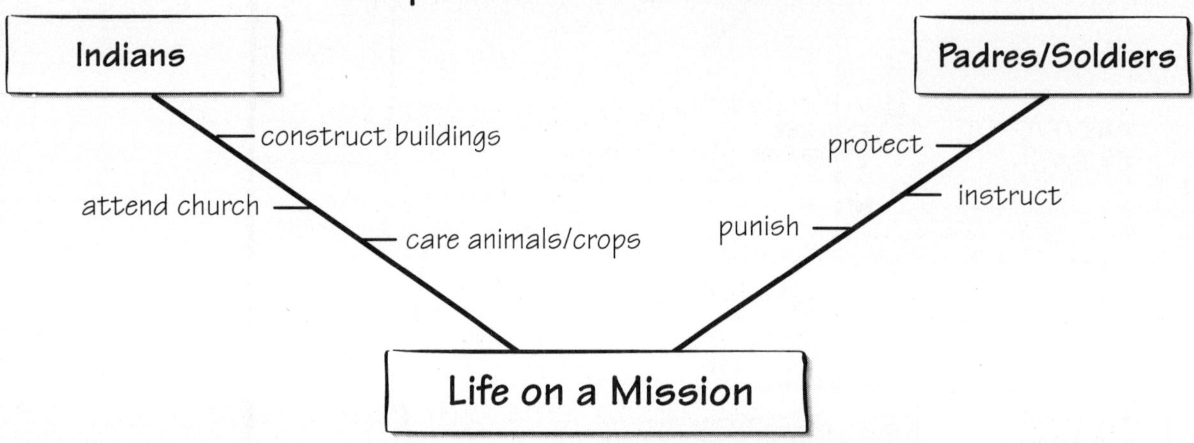

1. Look at the graphic overview above. Then answer the following question: On a mission, who did most of the hard, physical labor?

____

2. Read the lesson title and the red and blue headings in your text, pages 75–79. Use words from those headings to fill in the lesson outline below.

Life on a ______________

I. A Daily Routine

  A. ______________ To Be Done

II. ______________ of Mission Life

  A. Indians ______________

Name: Date:

CHAPTER 3

Lesson 4 Reading Strategy

Life on a Mission

(*Oh, California* pp. 71–74)

Using the Visuals This reading strategy helps you to use photographs, maps, charts, and illustrations to understand what you read. As you read, be sure to study the visuals and carefully read the captions.

1. **Look at the picture on page 75 and read the caption. What was this device used for? Circle the letter of your answer.**
   a. to wash and dry olives
   b. to press the juices from grapes
   c. to press the oil from olives

2. **Look at the small picture on page 76 and read the caption. Which list shows crops that the Spanish introduced to California? Circle the letter of your answer.**
   a. barley, oats, wheat, oranges
   b. grapes, wheat, strawberries
   c. corn, grapes, wheat, oats

3. **Look at the picture of the mission on pages 76–77 and read the caption. What can you learn from this picture?**

   ____

   ____

4. **Look at the "Indians at Mission in Monterey" graph on page 79 and read the caption. Complete the chart below.**

Graph Facts	Caption Facts

CHAPTER 3

Summary also on Audiotape

Lesson 4 Summary

Life on a Mission

(*Oh, California* pp. 75–79)

Thinking Focus: What were the daily routines on a Spanish mission?

A Daily Routine

The padres made the Indians use Spanish methods of **agriculture**. This included raising cattle, sheep, and chickens. It also included growing crops that had come from Spain, such as barley, oats, and wheat. The Spanish brought the first oranges to California. The padres also taught the Indians the Spanish language and **culture**. They were trying to turn the Indians into Spanish citizens.

Daily life on the mission followed a fixed plan. A ringing bell awoke everyone at sunrise. After breakfast and church, the work began. The Indians did all of the hard labor on the mission. This included farming, constructing and fixing buildings, and tanning leather. The padres did not pay the Indians for their work. Instead, they gave the Indians food, clothing, shelter, and religious training. At eleven, everyone had lunch and rested. Then they returned to work. Late in the day they had dinner and evening church services.

? What were some of the animals and crops grown on the missions?

agriculture
(ăg'rĭ-kŭl'chər)
the raising of crops and livestock

culture
(kŭl'chər)
the beliefs and way of life of a group of people

Summary continues on next page

Cruelty of Mission Life

Mission life was not easy for the Indians. Many were unhappy for the following reasons:

- They had to give up their culture and religious beliefs to learn Spanish culture and beliefs.
- They often lived in crowded, dirty conditions and were forced to do hard work.
- They were not allowed to leave the mission. If they left, they were brought back and punished.
- When crops failed, there wasn't enough to eat.
- Many Indians died of diseases brought to the Americas by the Spanish.

Some Indians tried to **revolt** against these conditions. In 1785, a woman named Toypurina helped warriors from six villages revolt against the San Gabriel Mission. She was arrested by the Spanish government. Indians at San Diego set a mission on fire and killed one of the padres. In 1824, the Chumash revolted at three missions near Santa Barbara.

revolt
(rĭ-vōlt′)
to fight against the government or other power

Father Serra's dream of having many missions had come true. But the growth of the missions was tragic for the California Indians. Thousands died. By the end of the 1800s, much of the Indian way of life had died also.

? Why did the Indians revolt against life on the missions?

Chapter Overview
Mexican California

Fill in the blank spaces below with information from the chapter.

When:
1810-1850

Where:
Alta California

Who:
The Mexican Government

Mexico Rules Alta California

Cause	Effect
Mexican War →	Californios begin to trade with countries other than ________________.
California Missions Close →	Way of life changes for ________________, ________________, and ________________.
Ranchos and Pueblos →	________________ and ________________ hold on to their Spanish way of life.

Name: Date:

CHAPTER 4

Lesson 1 Preview

Traders in California

(*Oh, California* pp. 86–89)

Development of Foriegn Trade in California
Initial Event
Mexican War for Independence
Event 2
Spain cuts off supplies.
Final Outcome
Californios barter with foreign traders.

1. **Study the graphic overview above to answer the following question: What two events led to foreign trade in California?**

2. **Look at the chart on page 89 of your text. Read the words under the heading *California*. Name the two most important things traders wanted in the early 1800s from the Californios.**

Name: Date:

CHAPTER 4

Lesson 1 Reading Strategy

Traders in California

(*Oh, California* pp. 86–89)

Cause and Effect This reading strategy helps you understand events and why they occur. As you read, think about the factors that caused an event. Then think about what the effects of that event may be.

1. Read the first three paragraphs on page 87. What caused the Mexican people from New Spain to go to war with Spain? Circle the letter of your answer.

a. Mexico wanted to trade with California.
b. The Mexican people wanted to be free of Spanish rule.
c. Spain would not let Mexico trade with California.

2. Read the section "Trading Ships Arrive" on page 87. What was the effect of the Mexican War?

a. California joined the war against Spain.
b. Other states joined the war against Mexico.
c. Spain could not afford to send supply ships to California.

3. What was another effect of the Mexican War?

____

4. Read the section "Hide and Tallow Trade Begins" on pages 88–89. Fill in the chart below.

Cause	Effect
Boston traders needed inexpensive leather for shoe factories in New England.	
	Trading ships brought to California things such as shoes, clothing, and spices.

CHAPTER 4

Lesson 1 Summary

Traders in California

(*Oh, California* pp. 86–89)

Summary also on Audiotape

Thinking Focus: Why was foreign trade important to the Californios?

War in Mexico Changes California

Before 1810, Spain did not allow ships from other countries to trade in Alta California. Spanish ships supplied all the goods. Then something happened to change trade in California.

The people from the part of New Spain that is now Mexico were unhappy with Spanish rule. They wanted better chances for jobs. They wanted to rule themselves. So Mexico decided to fight Spain for its **independence.**

independence (ĭn′dĭ-pĕn′dəns) when the people of a country or an area rule themselves

For 12 years, Spain and Mexico fought. Because of the cost of the war, Spain could not afford to send supply ships to Alta California. And it could not stop other countries from trading there. This meant that other countries could now trade with California settlers.

Russians came to California to hunt seals and otters. They built a fur-trading outpost north of San Francisco and traded clothing and tools for food. Trading ships also came from England and the United States. When the Mexican War ended, the Mexican rulers wanted these countries to keep trading with California.

[?] Why did the Mexican people want to be independent of Spanish rule?

Summary continues on next page

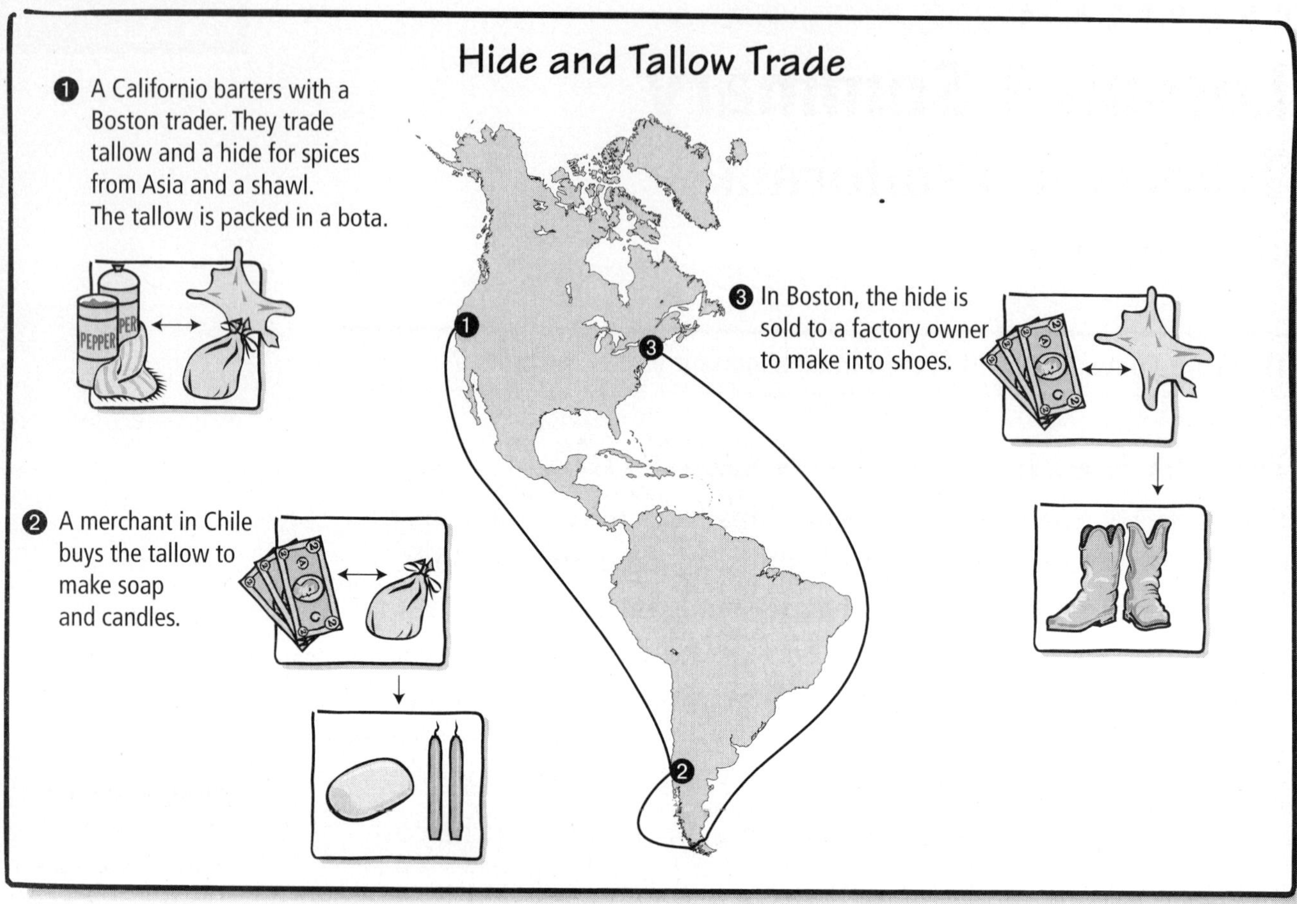

Hide and Tallow Trade
1 A Californio barters with a Boston trader. They trade tallow and a hide for spices from Asia and a shawl. The tallow is packed in a bota.
PEPPER
2 A merchant in Chile buys the tallow to make soap and candles.
3 In Boston, the hide is sold to a factory owner to make into shoes.

Hide and Tallow Trade Begins

Trading ships from Boston carried **products** the people in California needed such as shoes, clothing, and spices. The ship captains would **barter**, or trade, these goods for the cattle, hides, and tallow the Californios offered. Cattle hides, or skins, were used to make leather for shoes. The tallow, or fat from the cattle, was used to make candles and soap.

On the way back to Boston, trading ships stopped in Chile. There, they sold the tallow to merchants to make candles and soap. When the ships arrived in New England, they sold the hides to shoe factories. Other traders would then buy the shoes and sail back to California to barter for more hides and tallow.

product
(prŏd′əkt)
items that are made by people, machines, or nature

barter
(bär′tər)
to trade goods without using money

[?] How did Californios use hides and tallow?

Name: Date:

CHAPTER 4

Lesson 2 Preview

From Missions to Ranchos

(*Oh, California* pp. 90–93)

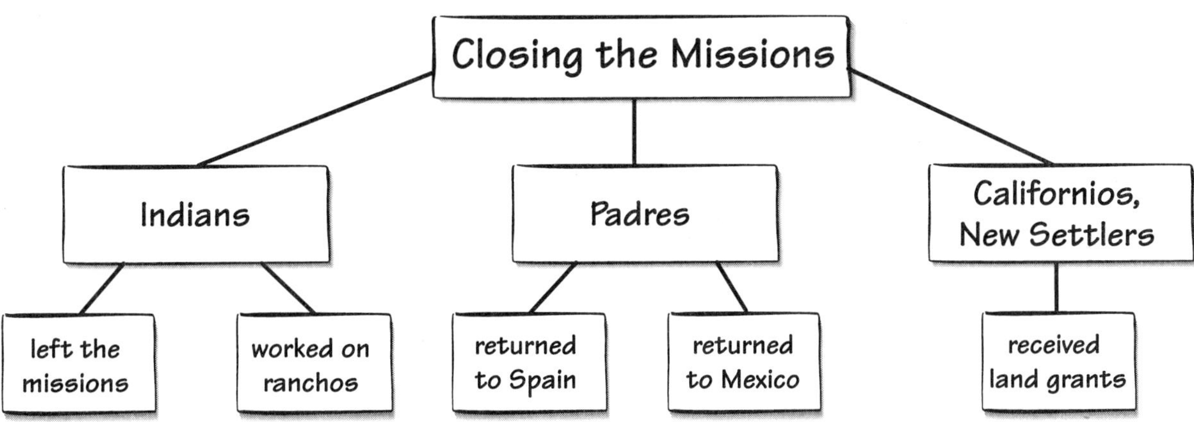

1. Study the graphic organizer above to answer the following questions:

a. What people were affected by the closing of the missions?

Indians, ____________________, and ____________________.

b. Who worked on ranchos?

____

2. Look at the map and map key on page 92 and the picture on page 93. Who do you think received the first land grants in California?

____

____

____

Name: Date:

CHAPTER 4

Lesson 2 Reading Strategy

From Missions to Ranchos

(*Oh, California* pp. 90–93)

Evaluate This reading strategy helps you recognize the difference between facts and opinions. A fact is something that can be proven to be true. An opinion is a belief based on what a person thinks or feels.

1. **Read page 90 and page 91 up to the blue head "Hardship for the Indians." Circle the statement below that is a fact.**
   a. The padres should not have gone back to Mexico.
   b. The Mexican government should not have closed the missions.
   c. The Mexican government divided the mission lands.

2. **Read the section "Hardship for the Indians" on page 91. Write two facts about the section.**

   ____

   ____

3. **Read the section "Ranchos and Rancheros" on pages 92–93. Then read the statements below and add them to the chart.**
   a. Women should not have been given land grants.
   b. Most ranchos were very large areas of grassland.
   c. Indians worked for the rich rancheros.
   d. Some rancheros did not grow rich.
   e. Small ranchos would have been better than big ranchos.

Fact	Opinion

4. **Read the section "Hardships on the Ranchos" on page 93. Then write one fact based on your reading.**

   ____

CHAPTER 4

Lesson 2 Summary

From Missions to Ranchos

(*Oh, California* pp. 90–93)

Summary also on Audiotape

Thinking Focus: How did the closing of the missions affect the Indians, the padres, and the new Mexican settlers?

End of the Missions

The new Mexican government got rid of many things connected with the old Spanish government. They closed the Spanish missions in California, and sent many padres back to Mexico or Spain. Then they divided the mission lands among the mission Indians, Californios, and Mexican settlers.

The Mexican government gave huge **land grants** to Californios and Mexican settlers. To get the grants, Californios and Mexicans had to make maps of their lands. They also had to prove they were Mexican citizens. Their lands became huge cattle ranches, or **ranchos.**

Mission Indians received only a little land. Some went back to the mountains or deserts to live. Others lost their land to dishonest settlers. The ranchos were on lands where the Indians used to hunt and gather food. So many Indians did not have enough to eat. They raided the ranchos and took the cattle. The Californios killed many of these Indians.

Other mission Indians found work on the ranchos. The men and boys worked as **vaqueros**, or cowboys. Indian women worked as housekeepers washing, cooking, and caring for children. These Indians did not gain their freedom when the missions closed. They just gained new masters, the **rancheros**, or ranch owners.

land grant
(lănd grănt)
a government gift of land

rancho
(răn'chō)
a cattle ranch

vaquero
(vä-kâr'ō)
a cowboy who worked on a rancho

ranchero
(răn-châr'ō)
the owner of a rancho

[?] What hardships did Indians face after the missions closed?

Summary continues on next page

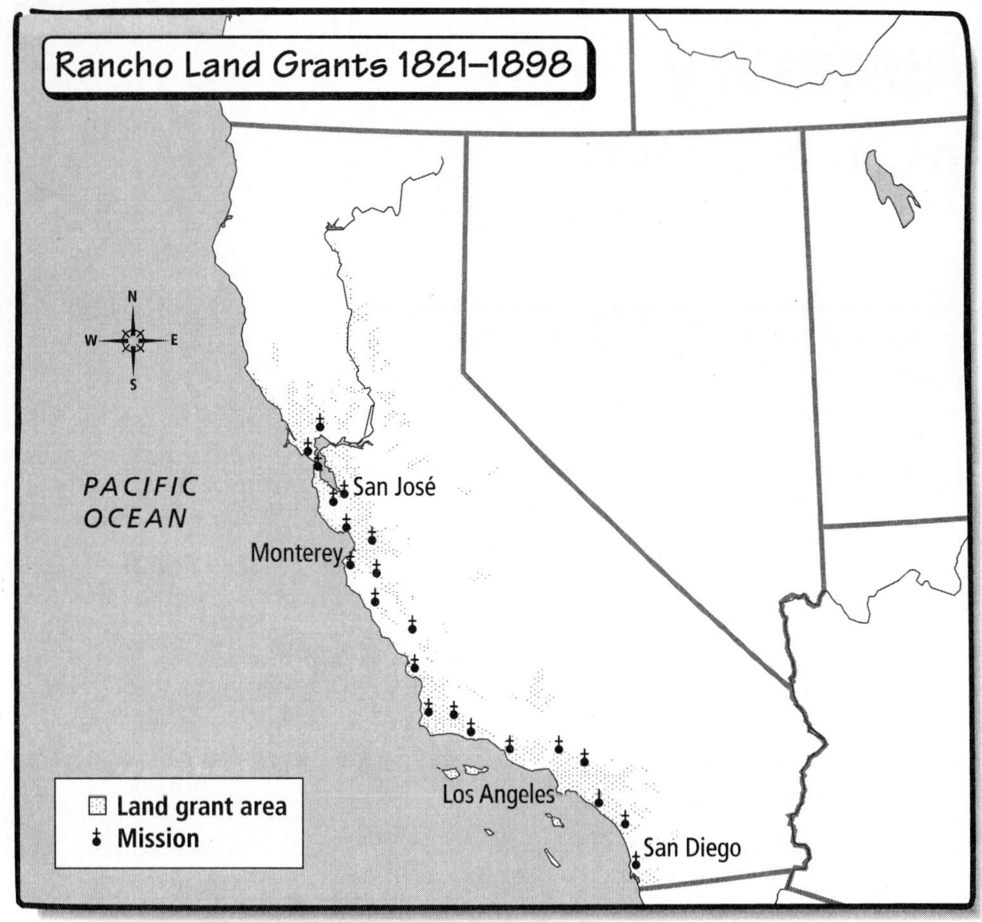

Ranchos and Rancheros

The first land grants went to men living in California. They were mostly soldiers, friends, or relatives of government officials. Later, Mexican citizens, men and women, applied for land grants. Most ranchos raised cattle for the hide and tallow trade. A lot of land was needed to raise cattle. A herd of 50 cows could eat a square mile of grass each year. So each rancho covered about 75 square miles of land.

Some rancheros became very rich. They lived in big houses. Often, a ranchero's entire family—grandparents, parents, aunts, uncles, and children—lived together. On these ranchos, Indian laborers did the work. Other rancheros were not rich. They had small herds of cattle or poor grazing land. They lived in small houses and did most of the work themselves.

[?] Explain why most ranchos were very large.

Name: ______________________ Date: ______________________

CHAPTER 4

Lesson 3 Preview

Ranchos and Pueblos

(*Oh, California* pp. 95–98)

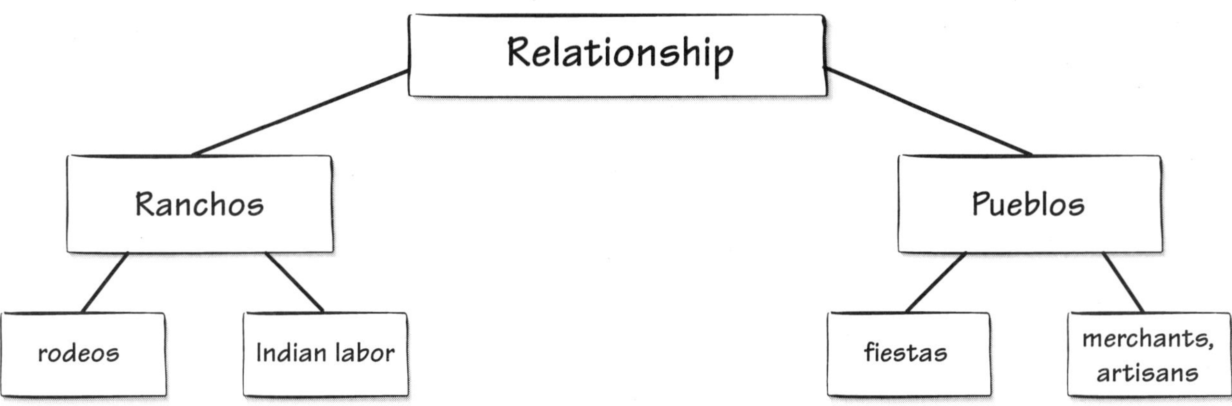

1. Study the graphic overview to complete the statements below.

a. Rodeos were held at ______________________.

b. ______________________ and ______________________ lived and worked in the pueblos.

2. Look at the pictures and captions on pages 95–98. Write one thing you expect to learn about life on a rancho and one thing you expect to learn about life in a pueblo.

____

____

____

____

____

____

____

____

Name: Date:

CHAPTER 4

Lesson 3 Reading Strategy

Ranchos and Pueblos

(*Oh, California* pp. 95–98)

Finding the Main Idea This reading strategy helps you organize and remember what you read. When you finish a selection, jot down the main idea and its supporting details.

1. **Read page 95. Write *M* next to the sentence that best tells the main idea of these paragraphs.**

   ___ Vaqueros sorted the free-roaming cattle.

   ___ During a rodeo, people gathered to rope, brand, and sort cattle.

   ___ People from the pueblo helped with the rodeo work.

2. **Read the section "Rancho Life" on page 96. Write *M* next to the sentence that best tells the main idea of this section.**

   ___ Workers made cloth and boiled tallow.

   ___ Indian women cooked meals.

   ___ Indian workers kept the ranchos running smoothly.

3. **Which sentences on page 96 are supporting details for the main idea: Indians worked on the ranchos?**

   ____

   ____

4. **Read the section "Pueblo Life" on page 98. Then fill in the chart.**

Main Idea	Supporting Details
The pueblo was the center of government and business for the rancheros.	

C H A P T E R 4

Summary also on Audiotape

Lesson 3 Summary

Ranchos and Pueblos

(*Oh, California* pp. 95–98)

Thinking Focus: How did the pueblos depend on the ranchos?

Rancho Life

Let's look at a ranchero and his family who live in a large adobe house. The nearest neighbor and pueblo are a day's ride away. There is no school nearby, so a tutor comes a few times a year to teach the children.

The ranchero tells the Indian vaqueros and laborers on the rancho what work needs to be done. Life on the rancho is filled with hard work. Indian workers take care of the animals, repair wagons and tools, cook the meals, weave cloth, and boil tallow to make soap and candles. The Indians keep the rancho running smoothly. Sadly, the Indians work for no pay. Instead, they are given food and alcohol.

[?] Describe daily life on a rancho.

Pueblo Life

Although rancheros were many miles from pueblos, they were part of pueblo life. Each pueblo had a few hundred adobe houses grouped around a wide **plaza**, or town square. Facing the plaza were these buildings:

- The town hall
- The church
- The rancheros' pueblo houses

The rancheros stayed in these houses when they came to trade cattle hides and tallow or to record their brands. A brand is a symbol burned into a cow's hide to identify its owner.

Saddlers, blacksmiths, innkeepers, and other workers lived and worked in the pueblo all year. They depended on the

plaza
(plä'zə)
a town square

Summary continues on next page

rancheros and traders for their business. The pueblos were run by a **town council**. The council chose an alcalde who acted as a mayor and judge.

Twice a year the alcalde declared a two-day holiday for a **rodeo**, or roundup. For months, cattle from different ranchos had roamed the land freely and mixed together. During the rodeo, the vaqueros rounded up the cattle and sorted them. New calves were given the brand of their rancho. After sorting and branding, hundreds of cattle were killed and skinned for their hides.

Everyone from the pueblo helped and celebrated with a fiesta, or festival. During a fiesta, people danced in the plaza, watched horse races, and enjoyed feasts. Fiestas were one of the Spanish traditions that Californios held onto.

? What was the importance of the ranchos to the pueblos?

town council
(toun koun'səl)
a group of elected officials who make the important decisions for a town

rodeo
(rō'dē-ō')
the roundup of a rancho's cattle

Chapter Overview
Newcomers from the United States

Fill in the blank spaces below with information from the chapter.

When:
1820–1856

Where:
California

Who:
Newcomers and Californios

Californios Face Change

Reasons Newcomers Came to California

________________ ________________ ________________

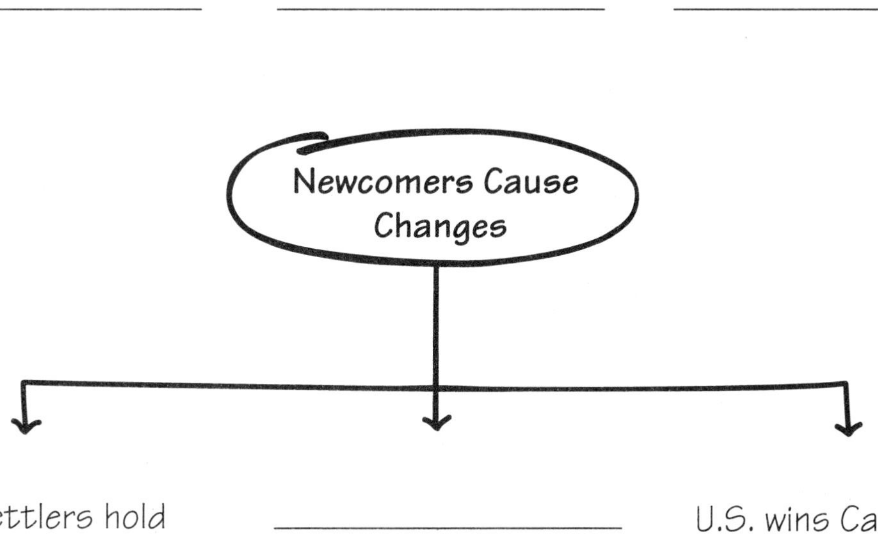

Name: Date:

CHAPTER 5

Lesson 1 Preview

Pioneers in California

(*Oh, California* pp. 108–111)

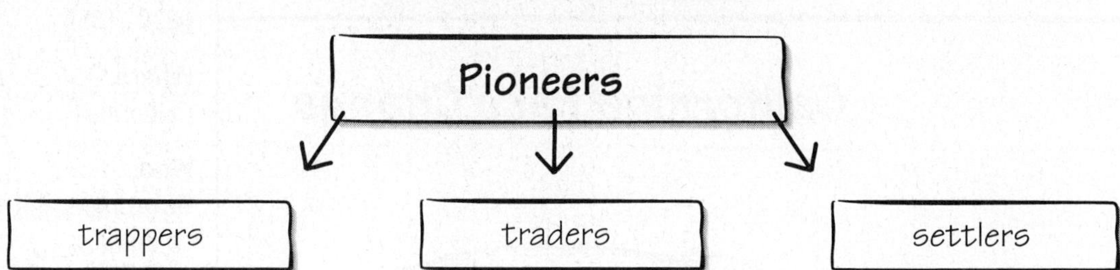

1. **Study the graphic overview above to complete the following sentence:**

   The pioneers in California were trappers, ____________________,
   and ____________________.

2. **Suppose you are a pioneer who is traveling overland to California from the East Coast between 1830 and 1850. Look at the map on page 109 in your text. In the area owned by Mexico, what two mountain ranges might you have to cross?**

Name: Date:

CHAPTER 5

Lesson 1 Reading Strategy

Pioneers in California

(*Oh, California* pp. 108–111)

Using the Visuals This reading strategy helps you to use photographs, maps, charts, and illustrations to understand what you read. As you read, be sure to study the visuals and carefully read the captions.

1. **Look at the pictures on pages 108 and 109 and read the captions. What can you learn about pioneers from the pictures and captions? Circle the best answer.**
   a. All pioneers lived among the Indians.
   b. Pioneers liked challenge and adventure.
   c. California welcomed the pioneers.

2. **Study the map on page 109. What can you learn about California from this map? Circle the best answer.**
   a. There were hundreds of trails in California.
   b. California was part of the United States.
   c. Mexico owned California and a large part of what is now the United States.

3. **Find all the mountain ranges shown on the map on page 109. Then look at the mountains pictured on page 110. Describe how hard it must have been for the pioneers to cross the mountains to get to California.**

   ____

4. **Look at all the illustrations and maps in the lesson. Use the information you find in the visuals and the captions to complete this chart.**

Reasons to Go to California	Overland Dangers	Sights

CHAPTER 5

Lesson 1 Summary

Pioneers in California

(*Oh, California* pp. 108–111)

Summary also on Audiotape

Thinking Focus: Why were pioneers from the United States attracted to California?

Growing Interest in California

During the 1820s, mountain men began to explore California. They included Jedediah Smith, James Beckwourth, and Abel Stearns.

In 1826, Jedediah Smith and two of his friends crossed the Mojave Desert into California. They were looking for adventure and for valuable beaver furs. They were the first people from what was then the United States to reach California by land. Mexican officials were afraid the United States wanted to take over California. They thought Smith was a spy and asked him to leave. Instead, Smith and his friends went north into the San Joaquin Valley. Then they went over the Sierra Nevada and became the first **pioneers** to cross this rugged mountain range.

Later, James Beckwourth found a pass through the Sierras. Beckwourth's Pass became an important route for miners and settlers heading to California.

In 1828, Abel Stearns set up a trading business in California and helped the Californios improve trade. He learned to speak Spanish, became a Mexican citizen, and married a Californio woman. The Mexican government knew he had not come to take over their land. So they welcomed him in California.

[?] Why did the Mexican government welcome Abel Stearns and not Jedediah Smith?

pioneer
(pī'ə-nîr')
a person who explores or settles land, showing the way for others to follow

Summary continues on next page

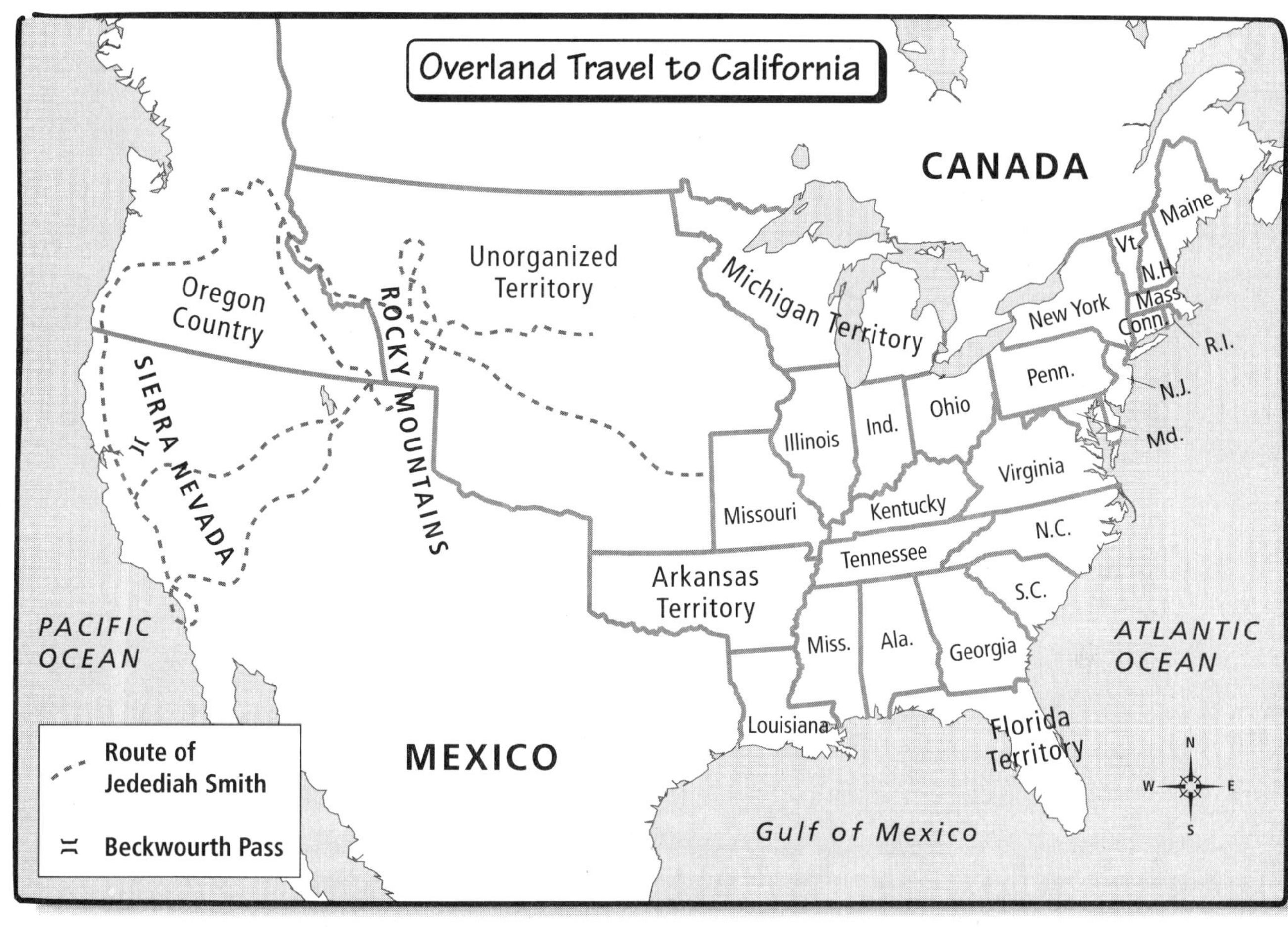

More Arrivals in California

During the 1830s and 1840s, hundreds of settlers headed to the California **frontier.** One settler, John August Sutter, became a Mexican citizen and received land from the Mexican government. He built a huge settlement that became an important stopping place for pioneers.

frontier
(frŭn-tîr′)
the land beyond the settled part of the country

Many stories told about the dangers of traveling west. In 1846, the Donner family led a wagon train of 87 settlers to California. When the settlers tried to take a shortcut through the mountains, they got lost. By the time they reached the Sierra Nevada, it was October. Snow already blocked their path. For seven months, the heavy snow trapped the settlers. There was so much snow they could not even hunt for food. When rescuers found them, only 47 settlers were still alive.

? What does the experience of the Donner Party tell you about traveling to California in the early 1840s?

Name: Date:

CHAPTER 5

Lesson 2 Preview

Mexico Defeated

(*Oh, California* pp. 116–120)

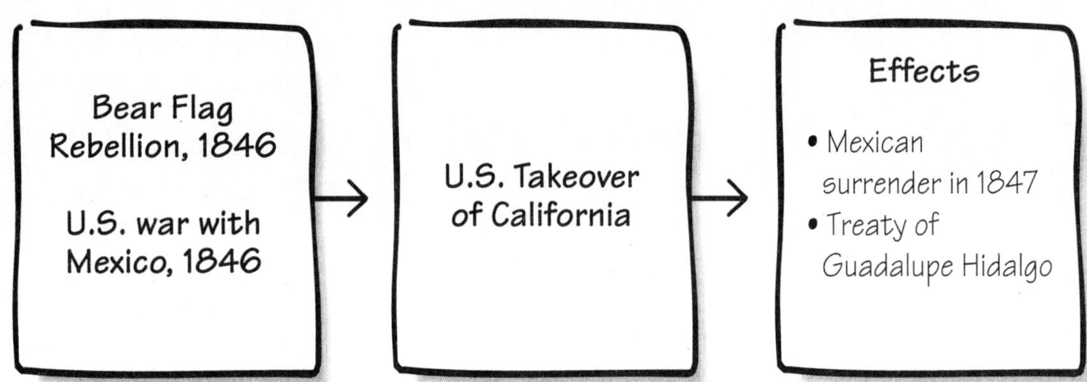

1. Look at the graphic organizer above, then read the following events. Circle the letter of the events that caused the United States takeover of California.

a. Treaty of Guadalupe Hidalgo, Bear Flag Rebellion of 1846

b. U.S. war with Mexico in 1846, Treaty of Guadalupe Hidalgo

c. Bear Flag Rebellion of 1846, U.S. war with Mexico in 1846

2. Look at the map on page 119 in your text. What does the orange area on the map show?

Name: ________________ Date: ________________

CHAPTER 5

Lesson 2 Reading Strategy

Mexico Defeated

(*Oh, California* pp. 116–120)

Self-Question This reading strategy helps you stay focused on what you read. Ask yourself questions before you read a section. Then read to see if you can find the answer to your questions.

1. **Read the heading "Revolt and War" on page 116. Look at the pictures on page 117 and read the captions. Check the question you think this section will answer.**

   ___ What happened to the Californios after the war?

   ___ Why did pioneers go to California?

   ___ What caused the Californians to revolt?

   Read the section to see if the question you chose was answered.

2. **Look at the map on page 119 and read the heading "California Captured" in the text. Write a question that asks about the map and the heading.**

   ____

3. **Read "The Change of Power" on page 119. Then look at the photograph on page 120 and read the picture caption. Write two questions in the chart you think this section will answer. Then read the section and answer the questions.**

My Questions	My Answers
1.	1.
2.	2.

CHAPTER 5

Lesson 2 Summary

Mexico Defeated

(*Oh, California* pp. 116–120)

Summary also on Audiotape

Thinking Focus: How did the United States gain control of California from Mexico?

Revolt and War

By 1846, about 2,000 settlers from the United States were living in California. The Californios wanted the settlers to follow the Californios' rules. This made the settlers angry.

One group of settlers decided to fight back. They tried to take over a Mexican fort at Sonoma. These **rebels** raised a flag showing a grizzly bear and the words "California Republic." The Bear Flaggers said they were at war with Mexico and were setting up a new **nation.**

Soon more settlers decided to help the rebels. Three hundred settlers came to Sonoma. At the time, this was a very large force. People thought that the Bear Flaggers could defeat the Mexican government in California.

Many people in the United States believed that their nation should rule all the land between the East and West coasts. So before the Bear Flag Revolt even began, the United States decided to declare war on Mexico.

rebel
(rĕb´əl)
a person who fights against the government

nation
(nā´shən)
a group of people ruled by one central government

[?] The 300 Bear Flag rebels might have been able to conquer California by themselves. What does this say about California in the 1840s?

Summary continues on next page

California Captured

The United States captured California in 1847, but the Mexican War went on until 1848. Finally, the United States and Mexico signed a **treaty** to end the war. In the Treaty of Guadalupe Hildago, Mexico agreed to give almost half its land to the United States. This land included California and was called the Mexican Cession.

Most Californios accepted the treaty. They could keep the land they owned before the war. They could even keep their own town governments. Although they were now United States citizens, little else changed. Most settlers looked forward to the peaceful life they had known before the war.

treaty
(trē´tē)
an official agreement between two or more countries

[?] Why might some settlers from the United States have wanted California to stay as it was before the war?

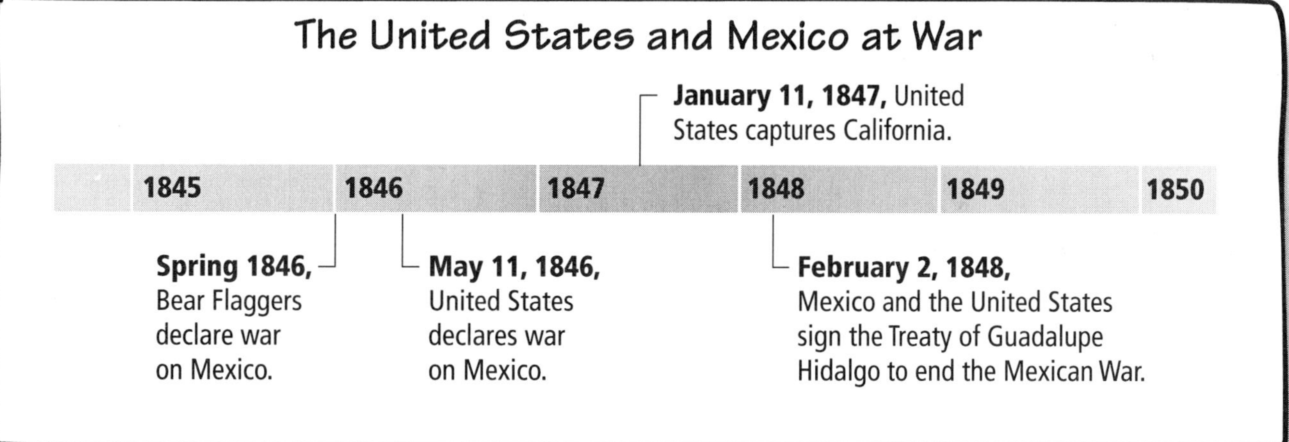
The United States and Mexico at War
January 11, 1847, United States captures California.
1845
1846
1847
1848
1849
1850
Spring 1846, Bear Flaggers declare war on Mexico.
May 11, 1846, United States declares war on Mexico.
February 2, 1848, Mexico and the United States sign the Treaty of Guadalupe Hidalgo to end the Mexican War.

Name: Date:

CHAPTER 5

Lesson 3 Preview

The Rush for Gold

(*Oh, California* pp. 121–124)

The California Gold Rush Begins

1. Look at the graphic overview above. Then write the words that best complete the sentences below.

a. ______________________ was discovered in California.

b. When news of the discovery spread, the ______________________ began.

2. Look at the cartoon on page 122. What does this cartoon of the gold rush show about the people and the event?

____

____

____

____

Name: Date:

CHAPTER 5

Lesson 3 Reading Strategy

The Rush for Gold

(*Oh, California* pp. 121–124)

Summarize This reading strategy helps you remember key points about what you have read. When you get to a good break in your reading, stop and write down the main ideas of what you have read.

1. **Read from the top of page 121 to the heading "The Rush Is On." Check the sentence that is the best summary of who first found gold near John Sutter's sawmill in California.**

   ___ "Indian Jim" found the gold while helping to build the sawmill.

   ___ James W. Marshall was the first to discover a gold nugget.

   ___ No one knows for sure who was the first to discover gold.

2. **Read the section "The Rush Is On" on pages 121–123. What is the best summary of how news of the gold rush spread?**

   ___ Californians heard reports of gold near Sutter's Fort.

   ___ Newspapers printed reports about California's gold.

   ___ Rumors among Californians, President Polk's speech, and worldwide newspaper reports spread the news of the gold rush.

3. **Read the section "The Overland Journey" on page 123. What is the best summary of the overland trip to California?**

   ___ The overland trip was costly but easy.

   ___ There were many problems and dangers in overland travel.

   ___ The overland trip was the best way to get to California.

4. **Read the sections "Sea Travel" and "The Panama Route" on page 124. Then write summary sentences to complete the chart.**

Sea Travel to California	The Panama Route to California

CHAPTER 5

Lesson 3 Summary

The Rush for Gold

(*Oh, California* pp. 121–124)

Summary also on Audiotape

Thinking Focus: What was the gold rush, and what did it mean to the United States and the world?

The Rush Is On

In 1848, gold was found in California near a sawmill owned by a man named John Sutter. Word about the discovery spread quickly. In San Francisco many workers left their jobs to look for gold. By late 1848, rumors of California gold reached the eastern United States. In December, newspapers carried the story to the rest of the world.

The year 1849 marked the beginning of the **gold rush.** In this year thousands of people came to California to look for gold. Some came from Mexico, Chile, and Peru. Others came from Europe and China. But most came from the United States—whites, African Americans, and Indians. The **forty-niners** were all looking for one thing—gold.

gold rush
(gōld rŭsh)
the years when large numbers of people came to California looking for gold

forty-niner
(fôr′tē-nī′nər)
a name given to people who came to mine gold in California

[?] Who were the forty-niners and where did they come from?

Summary continues on next page

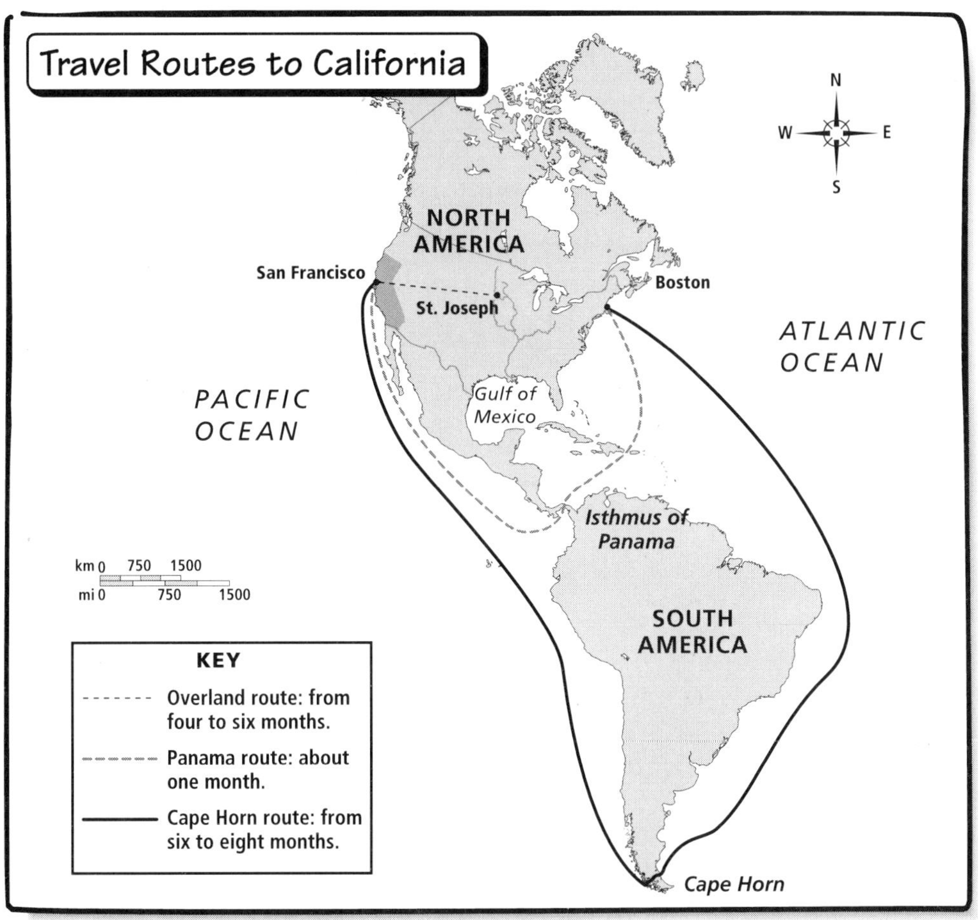

By Land and Sea

There were three ways for forty-niners to travel to California from the eastern United States:

- The least costly route was by land. This trip was long, hard, and filled with danger. Forty-niners crossed mountains, rivers, and deserts. Finding fresh water was a big problem. Many people died from drinking unsafe water.
- Some passengers sailed from the East around the southern tip of South America and then north to California. Ships were overcrowded, and the six-month trip was often boring and stormy. Many people got seasick.
- For the fastest route, forty-niners took a steamship to Central America. They crossed the **Isthmus** of Panama, and then took another steamship to California. This trip took about a month. But tickets were costly and hard to get, and the food was very bad.

isthmus
(ĭs´məs)
a narrow strip of land that connects two large sections

[?] What were the advantages and disadvantages of traveling through the Isthmus of Panama?

Name: ______________________ Date: ______________________

CHAPTER 5

Lesson 4 Preview

Gold Mining

(*Oh, California* pp. 125–129)

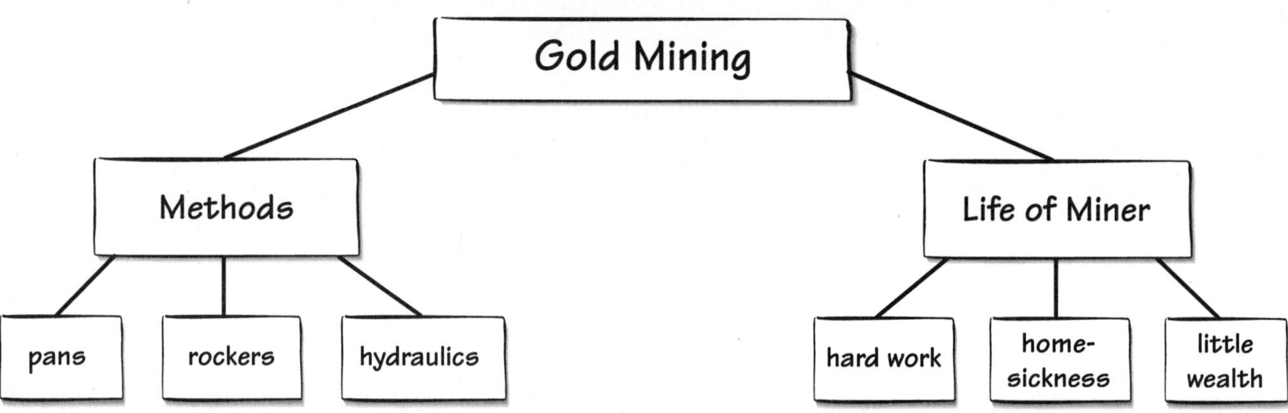

1. Look at the graphic organizer above, then read the sentences below. Fill in the missing words.

a. Miners had three ways of mining for gold. They could use pans, hydraulics, or ______________________.

b. In many ways, the life of a miner had little to offer. It was often a life of hard work, homesickness, and ______________________.

2. Look at the pictures on page 126. Think about what it would be like to mine for gold using these methods. Find at least one other picture in the lesson that shows how the forty-niners mined for gold. What was this method like?

____

____

____

____

Name: Date:

CHAPTER 5

Lesson 4 Reading Strategy

Gold Mining

(*Oh, California* pp. 125–129)

Think About Words This reading strategy helps you figure out the meaning of new words. When you come to an unfamiliar word, look for word parts you already know and use clues such as context and pictures.

1. **Read the section titled "Finding a Mine" on pages 125–126. Then read this sentence: To keep others away, miners placed *stakes* around their claims. What is a *stake?* What clues helped you understand the word?**

2. **Use word clues in "Finding a Mine" to find a word that means "to steal."**

3. **Read the section "The Panning Method" on page 126. Then look at the pictures at the top of the page. How do these pictures help you understand the meaning of the word *panning?***

4. **Look at the photographs on page 128 and read the captions. Fill in the chart to help you figure out what the word *nuggets* means.**

WORD: nuggets

Clues from the reading:

Clues from the pictures:

Similar words I already know:

Parts of words I already know:

The word means:

CHAPTER 5

Lesson 4 Summary

Gold Mining

(*Oh, California* pp. 125–129)

Summary also on Audiotape

Thinking Focus: What was it like to be a gold miner in gold rush California?

Finding a Mine

The best place to mine gold was along the rivers and streams that flowed down from the Sierra Nevada. Here, rain and melting snow carried bits of gold down from the mountains.

Most of the mining land belonged to the Indians. But that didn't stop the miners. They chased the Indians away. Sometimes they even killed Indians to get their land.

The land that belonged to a miner was called a **claim.** To keep others away from their land, miners put stakes around their claim. This was called "staking a claim." Some miners tried to "jump," or steal, a claim from others.

[?] Why did miners have to stake their claims?

claim
(klām)
the small piece of land on which a miner digs for gold

technology
(tĕk-nŏl′ə-jē)
new or better methods and ideas through science

Mining for Gold

The simplest way to mine gold was panning. Miners scooped up sand and water from the river with a flat-bottomed pan. Then they swirled the pan around to separate the gold from the sand. Miners also sometimes worked in pairs to use a simple machine called a rocker. Like panning, the rocker separated small bits of gold from the dirt and sand on the river bottom.

By the mid-1850s, most of the gold in California's rivers was gone. So mining companies used **technology** to find gold. Sometimes they used powerful hoses to spray water against mountains and riverbanks. This tore away huge pieces of earth. Then miners could get at the gold buried inside.

[?] What was one reason miners began to use more complicated machines for mining?

Summary continues on next page

Living in the Mines

As more miners came to California, many groups suffered. Indians were treated very unfairly. White traders charged them high prices. Rich mining companies only paid them with food and clothing. White miners chased them off their hunting lands. When the Indians tried to get the miners to leave, thousands were killed.

Other groups were also treated badly. Many white miners were jealous of Mexican miners, who were more successful at finding gold. They forced Chinese miners to live apart from whites.

Most miners did not find riches in the mines. Some went back East. Others stayed in California to begin new lives. These settlers worked on farms or ranches or in stores and businesses. They settled new towns and raised families.

? Besides the gold they found, what did the forty-niners contribute to California?

Chapter Overview
California Becomes a State

Fill in the blank spaces below with information from the chapter.

When:
1849-1870
Where:
present state borders of California
Who:
Californios, Indians, and Newcomers

Gold Rush Brings Changes to California

Changes in Cities and Towns

Population increase in cities

Crime increase in __________

People want __________

Changes in Government

Delegates hold __________

__________ is created

California becomes a __________

Changes in Law and Order

Crime gets worse in cities and towns

__________ groups form

Citizens become __________

Changes in Land Holdings

__________ move onto Californios' ranchos

Californios lose their __________

Indians lose their __________

Name: Date:

CHAPTER 6

Lesson 1 Preview

After the Gold Rush

(*Oh, California* pp. 134–137)

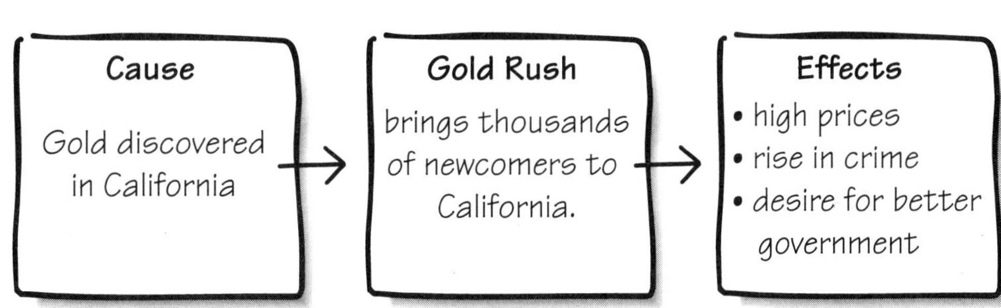

The Gold Rush
Cause
Gold discovered in California
Gold Rush
brings thousands of newcomers to California.
Effects
• high prices
• rise in crime
• desire for better government

1. Look at the graphic overview above, then choose from the words below to complete the sentence.

gold	government	crime

The thousands of newcomers to California brought a rise in ____________________ and a desire for better ____________________ for the state.

2. Look at the graph on page 137 of your text. Then answer the following question: About how many newcomers came to California between the years 1848 and 1850?

Name: Date:

CHAPTER 6

Lesson 1 Reading Strategy

After the Gold Rush

(*Oh, California* pp. 134–137)

Finding the Main Idea This reading strategy helps you organize and remember what you read. When you finish a selection, jot down the main idea and its supporting details.

1. **Read the section "San Francisco Faces Changes" on page 135. Write *M* by the sentence that best tells the main idea of the section.**

   ___ Many new buildings were poorly built.

   ___ As San Francisco's population grew, the city went through changes that were not all good.

   ___ There were not enough police officers to control all the people.

2. **Read the section "New Mining Towns" on page 136. Write a sentence that best tells the main idea of the section.**

   ____

3.–5. **Read the section "A Changing Government" on pages 136 and 137. Then complete the chart by listing three supporting details.**

Main Idea	Supporting Details
Californios and Americans were both worried about California and wanted to do something to improve the conditions there.	1. 2. 3.

CHAPTER 6

Lesson 1 Summary

After the Gold Rush

Summary also on Audiotape

(*Oh, California* pp. 134–137)

Thinking Focus: In what ways did the gold rush change California?

A Flood of Miners

The gold rush brought big changes to San Francisco. By 1850, the town had grown from 500 people to 35,000. People came from countries around the world and from many parts of the United States. Soon, there were so many people the police could not control them all. Many people began to worry about the lack of order in the city.

Mifflin Gibbs was one of many free blacks who came to California during this time. He worked hard and opened his own business. Gibbs wanted to end the unfair treatment of blacks in the United States. He began a newspaper called *Mirror of Our Times* to write about his ideas.

Some California towns grew because miners bought their supplies there. Other towns were brand new, built by the miners. At first, the mining towns were peaceful. But as they became more crowded, some miners decided it was easier to steal gold than dig for it. Claim jumping became a big problem. Fighting among miners increased. Life in mining towns became dangerous. Many of these towns disappeared when the gold ran out. But some still exist today.

[?] What effect did the forty-niners have on California's cities and towns?

Summary continues on next page

A Changing Government

Californios were worried about their growing state. They felt the miners, whom they called Americanos, were treating them badly and acted as if the state belonged to them. The Americanos forced the Californios from their mining claims and made them feel unwelcome on their own land.

The Americanos were also worried about California. They did not like the crime and living conditions in the cities. They wanted California to be a state, so they could vote for leaders who would work to improve these conditions.

General Bennet Riley was the United States official in charge of California in 1849. He called an election so the Californios and Americanos could choose **delegates** to speak and act for both groups of citizens. The delegates held a **convention** to decide California's future.

delegate
(dĕl′ĭ-gāt′)
a person who is chosen to act or speak for another person or a group

convention
(kən-vĕn′shən)
a large gathering of people with the same interests who meet to discuss important issues

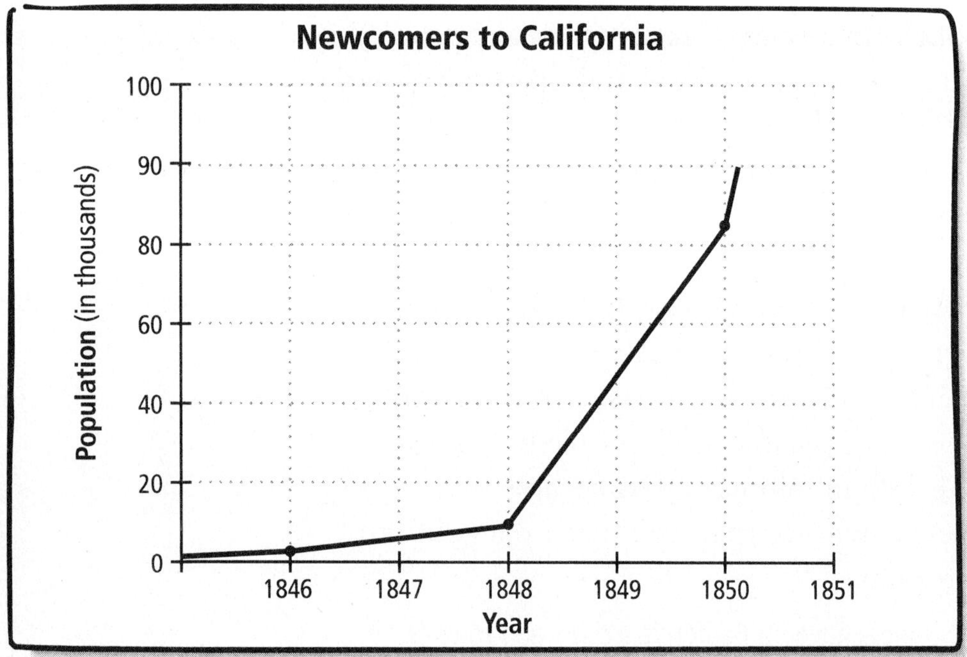

[?] Summarize the concerns of the Californios and the newcomers from the United States.

Name: Date:

CHAPTER 6

Lesson 2 Preview

The Thirty-first State

(*Oh, California* pp. 141–145)

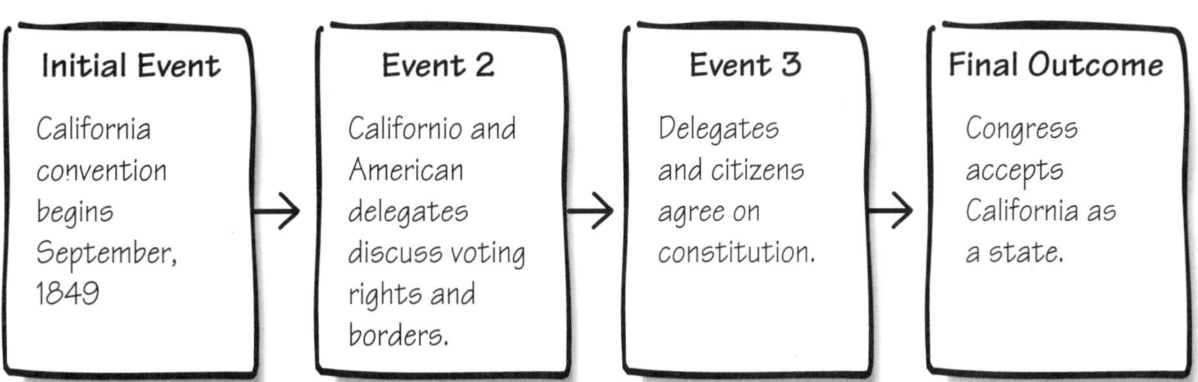

Moving Toward Statehood
Initial Event
California convention begins September, 1849
Event 2
Californio and American delegates discuss voting rights and borders.
Event 3
Delegates and citizens agree on constitution.
Final Outcome
Congress accepts California as a state.

1. Look at the graphic overview above. Then read the following list of events. Place the events in order by writing numerals 1, 2, 3, or 4 in the blank before each event.

   ___ Delegates and citizens agree on a constitution.

   ___ Delegates discuss voting rights and borders.

   ___ Congress accepts California as a state.

   ___ California convention begins.

2. Look at the map on page 142. What is California's western border?

   ____

   ____

Name: Date:

CHAPTER 6

Lesson 2 Reading Strategy

The Thirty-first State

(*Oh, California* pp. 141–145)

Summarize This reading strategy helps you remember key points about what you have read. When you get to a good break in your reading, stop and write down the main ideas of what you have read.

1. **Read the sections "A Natural Border" and "Two Californias" on pages 142 and 143. Check the best summary of these sections.**

   ___ California was divided into two sections—a southern part and a northern part.

   ___ California would include all the land from the Mexican Cession.

   ___ To make it easier to govern, Californians chose the Sierra Nevada and the Colorado River as the eastern border.

2. **Read "Voting Rights." Write the best summary of who would be able to vote in California.**

   ____

3. **Read the first two paragraphs under the section "The Task Is Finished" on pages 143 and 144. Write a short summary of this section.**

   ____

   ____

4. **Read the sections "Congress Accepts California" and "Biddy Mason Wins Her Freedom" on pages 144 and 145. Complete the chart to summarize events.**

Congress Accepts California	Biddy Mason Wins Her Freedom

Lesson 2 Summary
The Thirty-first State

(*Oh, California* pp. 141–145)

Summary also on Audiotape

Thinking Focus: How did the constitutional convention change California?

The Convention Begins

The first California convention was held on September 3, 1849. Together, Americanos and Californios made decisions about California's future. They first decided how big California should be. The land had been part of a large area Mexico gave to the United States after the Mexican War. Some delegates wanted California to cover most of this land. Other delegates thought the state should be split into two sections, a northern part and a southern part. Californios lived mostly in the southern part. Americanos lived mostly in the northern part. The delegates finally agreed that California should stay as one area.

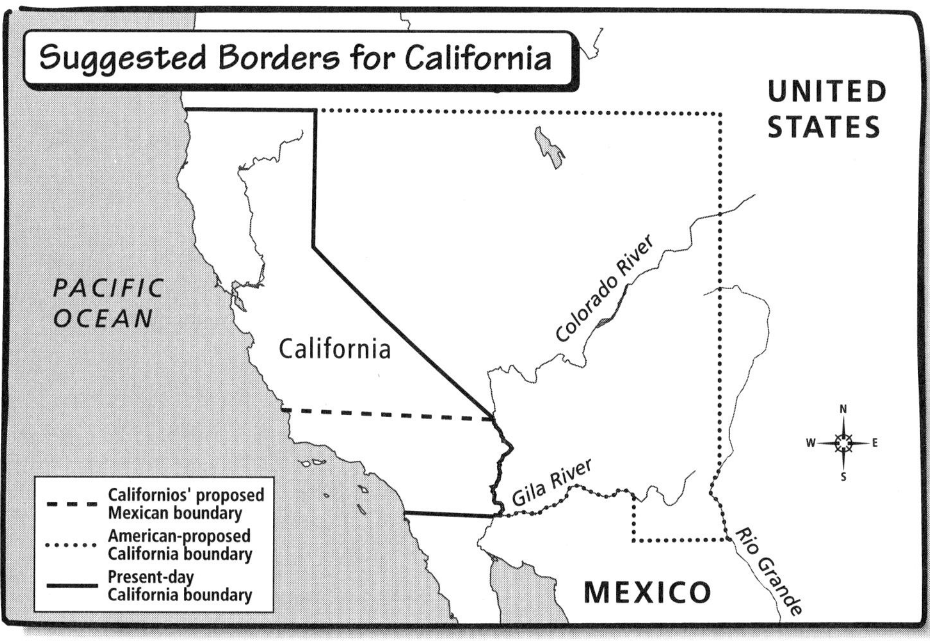

Summary continues on next page

Delegates also decided who could vote in California. Many Americanos did not want Indians to be able to vote. The Californios disagreed. One of their delegates, Manuel Dominguez, had Indian roots. The delegates decided that Dominguez could vote. But other Indians were denied voting rights until many years later. Black Americans, women, and Chinese Americans were also denied voting rights.

[?] Why did the Californios and the Americanos differ on the topics of borders and voting rights?

The Task Is Finished

Delegates also gave women the right to own land. In 1849, no other state did this. They decided California would not allow **slavery.** On October 12, 1849, they signed a **constitution** that listed their decisions. The U. S. Congress approved it on September 9, 1850. California became the thirty-first state.

California's constitution helped people like Biddy Mason. Mason was an enslaved black American who lived in California. When her owner, Robert Smith, heard that California did not allow slavery, he planned to move. Mason told two free black businessmen of Smith's plans. They had Smith brought to court. When Smith failed to come to court, the judge declared Mason free. Biddy Mason became a leading citizen of Los Angeles. She was the first black woman to own land in the city. She also helped the poor and founded a church for her community.

[?] What good and bad opinions might Biddy Mason have had about California's constitution?

slavery
(slā´və-rē)
a system of forced labor in which people work without pay for others who act as their masters

constitution
(kŏn´stĭ-too͞´shən)
an official agreement that lists the rules and government duties for a state or country

Summary continues on next page

Name: Date:

CHAPTER 6

Lesson 3 Preview

Law and Order

(*Oh, California* pp. 146–149)

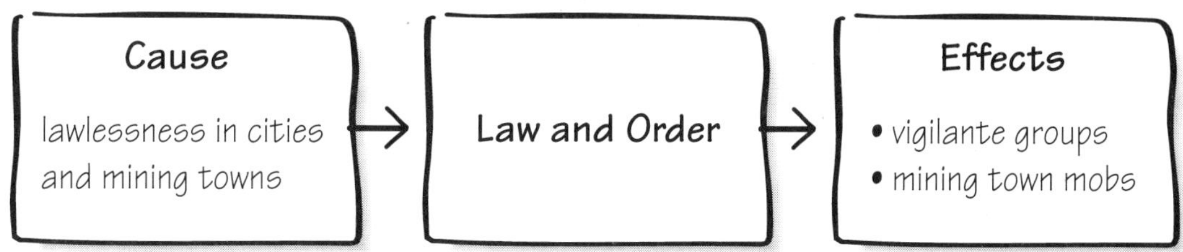

1. Look at the graphic overview above. Then answer the question: What caused vigilante groups and mobs in the mining towns to form?

____

2. Look at the picture on page 149 and read the caption. How do you think the miners solved crime problems quickly?

____

____

____

Name: Date:

CHAPTER 6

Lesson 3 Reading Strategy

Law and Order

(*Oh, California* pp. 146–149)

Cause and Effect This reading strategy helps you understand events and why they occur. As you read, think about the factors that caused an event. Then think about what the effects of that event may be.

1. **Read the lesson opener on page 146. What effect did the name Joaquin have on Californians? Circle the letter of your choice.**
   a. It sent chills up people's spines and made them fearful.
   b. It made people laugh and cry.
   c. It made people cheer to hear his name.

2. **As the legend goes, what caused Joaquin to turn to a life of crime?**

   ___

3. **Read the section "Crime in California" on page 147. What caused the citizens in the towns to capture and punish criminals themselves?**
   a. They felt they could take care of crime better than the courts could.
   b. They believed that the judges were also criminals.
   c. They knew that there were not enough police to control the people.

4. **What was the effect of the vigilante groups on some people?**

   ___

5. **Read the section "Mining Town Trouble" on pages 148 and 149. Then fill in the chart below.**

Cause	Effect
Miners did not want to wait for sheriffs to travel to their mining towns to settle problems.	
	The French and Chilean miners suspected of robbery and murder could not tell their side of the story.

CHAPTER 6

Lesson 3 Summary

Law and Order

(*Oh, California* pp. 146–149)

Thinking Focus: How did Californians try to keep peace and order in their new state?

Crime in California

California was now a state. But it still did not have order in its cities and towns. Murders, fights, and robberies were common. San Francisco was especially wild. When a popular newspaper reporter, James King, was killed because of a story he wrote, citizens became angry. They took the murderer, James Casey, and hanged him.

These citizens were **vigilantes**, people who punished someone without having the right to do so. The vigilantes' group became popular in San Francisco. More than 6,000 people joined the group. They did not care about **justice**. They broke the **law** by doing what they wanted. Soon other towns formed their own vigilante groups.

vigilante
(vĭj´ə-lăn´tē)
a person who captures and punishes people without having the right to do so

justice
(jŭs´tĭs)
the fair and equal treatment of all people

law
(lô)
a set of rules that all people must obey

[?] Why do you think so many citizens joined the vigilantes, even though the vigilantes broke the law?

Mining Town Trouble

Crimes like stealing and fighting were also bad in mining towns. These towns were located far from police and sheriffs. Miners wanted to spend their time digging for gold. So they punished people quickly instead of waiting for the sheriff. The miners ignored justice.

That's what happened in the mining town of Old Dry Diggings. One January day, a group of 200 miners hanged three men for a robbery and murder. Two of the men were from France, and one was from Chile. None of the men spoke English.

Summary continues on next page

They could not tell their side of the story. They did not even know why they were being punished. When people learned of the hangings, the town became known as Hangtown.

By taking the law into their own hands and ignoring justice, the miners and the vigilantes were just as guilty of breaking the law as the accused were.

[?] The three men who were hanged at Hangtown did not speak or understand English. Why is this important?

Summary continues on next page

Name: Date:

CHAPTER 6

Lesson 4 Preview

Californios and Indians Lose Their Land

(*Oh, California* pp. 155–157)

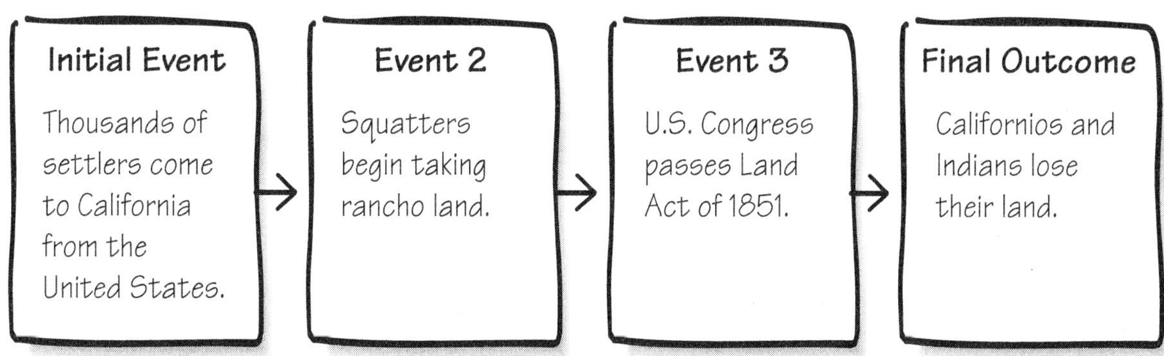

Newcomers Change California
Initial Event
Thousands of settlers come to California from the United States.
Event 2
Squatters begin taking rancho land.
Event 3
U.S. Congress passes Land Act of 1851.
Final Outcome
Californios and Indians lose their land.

1. Look at the graphic overview above, then read the following list of events. Place the events in order by writing 1, 2, 3, and 4 in the blank before each event.

___ U.S. Congress passes Land Act of 1851.

___ Thousands of settlers come to California from the United States.

___ Californios and Indians lose their land.

___ Squatters begin taking rancho land.

2. Look at the old map and read the caption on page 156. What do the map and caption tell you about the size of ranchos in California?

Name: ______________________ Date: ______________________

CHAPTER 6

Lesson 4 Reading Strategy

Californios and Indians Lose Their Land

(*Oh, California* pp. 155–157)

Sequence This reading strategy helps you follow what is happening in your reading. As you read, pay attention to dates and times, as well as to words such as *before, finally, after,* and *then.*

1. **Read the first two paragraphs under "Rancheros Lose Their Lands." Place the events in order by writing 1, 2, and 3 in the blanks.**

   ___ Some rancheros gave up and sold their ranchos.

   ___ There were so many squatters, neither the rancheros nor the police could keep them off rancheros' land.

   ___ Some Americans move onto the ranchos and start their own farms.

2. **Read the paragraphs under the head "The Government Acts." Check the event that came first in each pair.**

   a. ___ Congress passes the Land Act of 1851.

   ___ Rancheros must prove that they are the rightful landowners.

   b. ___ The commission usually rules in favor of the rancheros.

   ___ Rancheros sell their land in order to survive.

3. **Read the first paragraph under "Indians Lose Their Land and Their Lives." What helps you understand the sequence of events?**

   ____

4. **Read to the end of the lesson on page 157. Complete the timeline below with the dates and events.**

late 1700s	___________	1851–1852
Indians are forced from coastal lands to make way for ___________ and ___________.	Miners force Indians from the ___________ foothills, often hunting and killing them.	The United States tries to work out land ___________ with the Indians, but ___________.

CHAPTER 6

Lesson 4 Summary

Californios and Indians Lose Their Land

(*Oh, California* pp. 155–157)

Summary also on Audiotape

Thinking Focus: How did the Californios and Indians lose their land?

Rancheros Lose Their Land

Californios had lived on ranchos since the days of Mexican rule. But American settlers were angry when they saw the ranchos. They felt one rancho of 40,000 acres was big enough for hundreds of farms. Some settlers, called **squatters**, moved onto the ranchos and started farms. There were so many squatters the Californio rancheros could not stop them. Even though the squatters were breaking the law, the police and courts could not stop them all either. Finally, some Californios sold their ranchos. Others lost their ranchos when they could not pay their debts. They lost their ranchos to the people who had loaned them money to buy more land.

squatter
(skwŏ´tər)
a person who lives or farms on someone else's land without permission

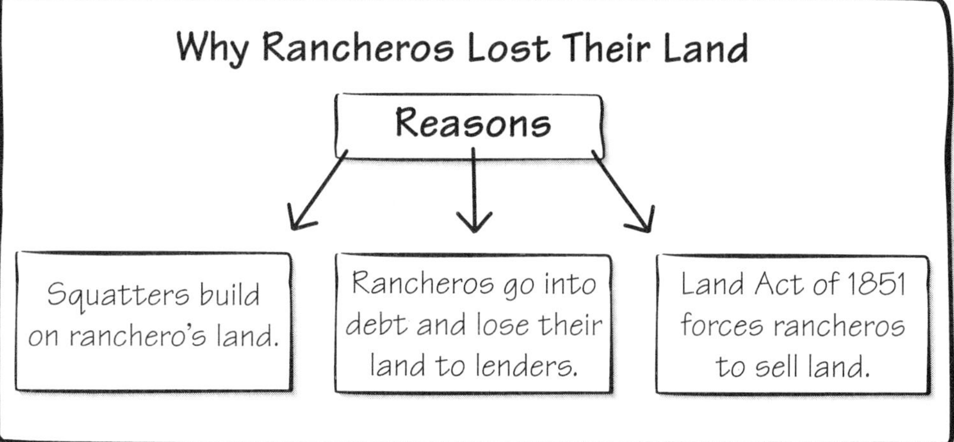

Why Rancheros Lost Their Land
Reasons
Squatters build on ranchero's land.
Rancheros go into debt and lose their land to lenders.
Land Act of 1851 forces rancheros to sell land.

Summary continues on next page

Another threat to the rancheros was the Land Act of 1851. This act set up a **commission** to decide whether the Californios really owned their ranchos. It was hard for many rancheros to prove they were the rightful owners. Many did not understand English. They had to hire lawyers to help them. Sometimes these lawyers cheated the rancheros out of their land. The Land Commission usually ruled in favor of the rancheros. But the Commission took 17 years or longer to decide each case. Many rancheros spent all their money on lawyers. They had to sell their land to survive.

commission
(kə-mĭsh´ən)
a group of people chosen to do a certain job

? Why were the Californios unable to stop the squatters from taking their land?

Indians Lose Their Land and Their Lives

Californios lost their ranchos. Indians lost much more. Indians had already been forced from the California coast by the Spanish. Later, miners and settlers took Indian lands in the Sierra Nevada foothills. There, Indian groups were hunted and killed. State laws even made it possible to capture Indians and make them slaves.

In 1851–1852, the United States government tried to work out treaties. These treaties would give the Indians millions of acres of land if they promised to give up the state land. But many people thought the land might have gold on it. They stopped the treaty process. The government finally moved about 2,000 Indians to reservations with few natural resources. The other 98,000 Indians in California had to try to survive on the poorest land in the state.

? What happened to the Indians in the 1850s?

Summary continues on next page

Chapter Overview
The Transcontinental Railroad

Fill in the blank spaces below with information from the chapter.

When:
1850–1869

Who:
Theodore Judah,
The Big Four,
Chinese and Irish immigrants

The Railroad Changes California

California Cut Off from Rest of United States

↓

Theodore Judah Dreams of a Transcontinental Railroad

↓

____

↓

____

↓

New Markets for California Businesses and Farms

Name: _______________ Date: _______________

CHAPTER 7

Lesson 1 Preview

Linking California to the East

(*Oh, California* pp. 164–167)

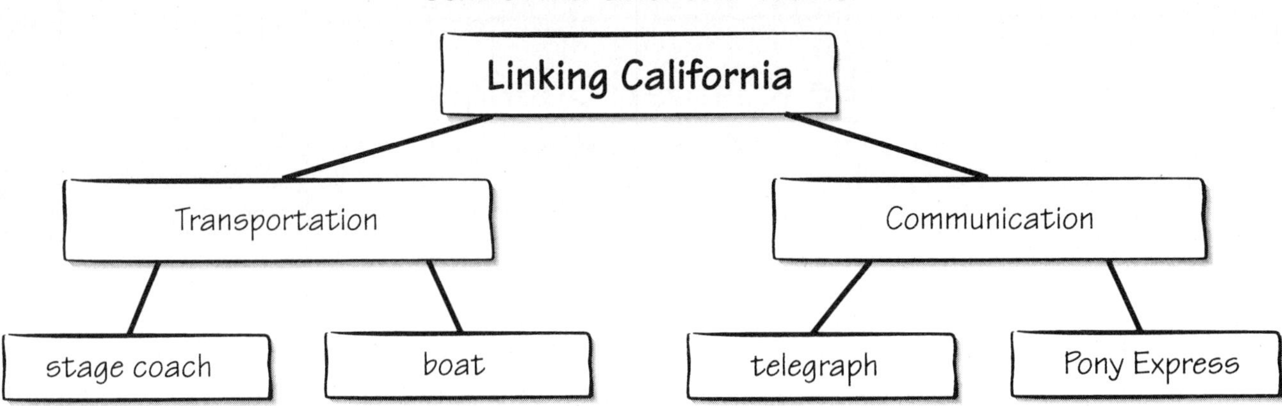

1. **Look at the graphic organizer above, then fill in the missing words in the sentences below.**

   a. The _______________ and the _______________ were two ways of communicating that helped to link California with the rest of the world.

   b. The _______________ and the _______________ were two means of transportation that helped to link California with the rest of the world.

2. **The Californians of the 1850s felt cut off from the rest of the United States. Look at the map on page 165 of your text and read the map legend. Write a sentence explaining why the people of California may have felt this way.**

____

____

____

____

____

____

Name: Date:

CHAPTER 7

Lesson 1 Reading Strategy

Linking California to the East

(*Oh, California* pp. 164–167)

Using the Visuals This reading strategy helps you to use photographs, maps, charts, and illustrations to understand what you read. As you read, be sure to study the visuals and carefully read the captions.

1. **Look at the map and map key on page 165 and read the caption. What does this map show? Circle the best answer.**
   a. the travel times from the eastern states to California
   b. the travel routes and times from the eastern states to California
   c. the travel routes from the eastern states to California

2. **Look at the graphic at the bottom of page 165 and read the captions. What can you learn from them?**

   ____

3. **Study the Morse code and the graphic on page 166. Write *California* in Morse code.**

   ____

4. **Look at the map and map key on page 167. Read the caption. Write a sentence to answer the question in the caption.**

   ____

5. **Read the description on page 166 of how an operator used a telegraph to send a message. Complete the chart to tell what you learned.**

What I Learned

____

____

____

____

CHAPTER 7

Summary also on Audiotape

Lesson 1 Summary

Linking California to the East

(*Oh, California* pp. 164–167)

Thinking Focus: Why did Californians in the 1850s and early 1860s feel cut off from the other states?

California Feels Cut Off

Abraham Lincoln's first speech as President reached California by Pony Express. Starting out in Nebraska, Pony Express riders carried the news to California. But the speech was two weeks old when it got there. **Communication** with California was very slow.

Transportation from the East to California was even slower. Wagon trains took four to six months or more. Travel by boat was about six months. Even the shortest route, across the Isthmus of Panama, took at least a month. The long trip raised the price of goods shipped to California. It also made Californians feel cut off from the rest of the country.

People began looking for better ways to get goods and messages to California. Here are a few of their ideas:

- One company tried using camels to carry goods across the hot, dry desert. But the camels got sore feet from the cactus plants.
- John Butterfield began the Butterfield Stage Line between California and the Mississippi River. The trip took 24 days. The stages carried mail, packages, and people.
- In 1861, workers finished setting up telegraph wires across the country. Telegraph operators used Morse code to send messages from coast to coast in a matter of minutes.

People also dreamed of having a **transcontinental** railroad that would link California with the rest of the country. But how could the railroad be built across the mountains? And who would pay the millions of dollars it would cost?

communication
(kə-myōō´nĭ-kā´shən)
the sending of news, messages, and information

transportation
(trăns´pər-tā´shən)
the movement of people and goods from place to place

transcontinental
(trăns´kŏn-tə-nĕn´tl)
something that reaches from one side of a continent to another

Summary continues on next page

If you lived in California, how long it might take...

For a letter to reach a friend in Boston	For a birthday gift to reach your aunt in New York	For inaugurational news to reach Washington D.C.	For you and your family to move to Philadelphia
1861 Two weeks by Pony Express	**1861** Six months by ship	**1861** Two weeks by Pony Express	**1861** Nine months by wagon train
Today Two days by US Mail	**Today** Seven days by US Mail	**Today** Instantly by TV and radio	**Today** Six hours by plane

[?] Even with the Butterfield Stage and the telegraph, Californians were still not satisfied. Why not?

Civil War Begins

In the summer of 1861, the Civil War began. The southern states had broken away from the United States over the issue of slavery. The South called its new country the Confederate States of America. The northern states, called the Union, wanted to keep all the states together. California sided with the Union.

During the war, California felt even more cut off from the East. The Union and Confederate armies needed all the food and goods the East could supply. Goods to California slowed down. More than ever, Californians needed better ties with the rest of the nation. More than ever, they needed a transcontinental railroad.

[?] What effect did the Civil War have on California?

Name: _______________ Date: _______________

CHAPTER 7

Lesson 2 Preview

The Railroad Is Born

(*Oh, California* pp. 168–171)

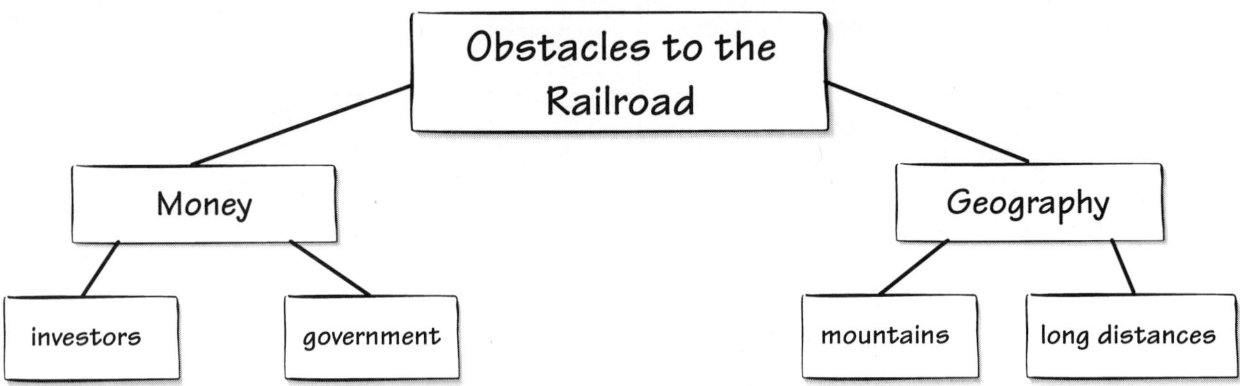

1. **Look at the graphic overview above, then write the words that best complete each sentence below.**

   a. To build the transcontinental railroad, money was needed from people and the ____________________.

   b. Building a railroad across mountains and over ____________________ would not be easy.

2. **Look at the photograph on page 168. It shows the mountains the transcontinental railroad would cross. The map on page 169 shows the route the railroad would follow. Write a sentence to describe the route.**

____

____

____

____

____

____

____

Name: Date:

CHAPTER 7

Lesson 2 Reading Strategy

The Railroad Is Born

(*Oh, California* pp. 168–171)

Predict/Infer This reading strategy helps you understand what you have read and what you will read next. Before you read a section, think about the titles, pictures, and captions. Then think about what will happen in the selection.

1. **Read the lesson title and opening paragraphs on page 168. Then look at the photograph and read its caption. What do you predict will be the main topic of the section "Following a Dream"? Check your prediction.**

   ___ Theodore Judah will give up his dream of building a railroad.

   ___ The people of California will not want Judah to succeed.

   ___ Theodore Judah will find a way to build his railroad.

2. **Name a clue that helped you make your prediction.**

   ___

3. **Read the blue head on page 169 and the first two paragraphs that follow. Make a prediction of what will happen next.**

   ___

4. **How did what you have learned so far about Judah and his dream help you to make your prediction?**

   ___

5. **Look at the map and read the captions on page 170. Then read the first two paragraphs under the section "Pushing Judah Out." Then fill in the chart below.**

What I Know	What I Predict

C H A P T E R 7

Lesson 2 Summary

The Railroad Is Born

(*Oh, California* pp. 168–171)

Thinking Focus: What problems did Theodore Judah and the Big Four have to solve before they could build the transcontinental railroad?

Following a Dream

More than anything else, Theodore Judah dreamed of building a transcontinental railroad. So he set out to prove that the railroad could cross the rugged Sierra Nevada. Judah and his assistant, Daniel Strong, hiked through the Sierra Nevada. They wanted to **survey**, or measure, the height of the mountains. The trip was a success. The two men found a good route for the railroad to follow.

To raise money for the railroad, Judah met with four California businessmen. Judah asked them to **invest** in his Central Pacific Railroad Company. In return, the men would make money if the railroad company did well. The men's decision to invest was a wise one. They earned so much money from the railroad company that they became known as the Big Four.

Judah also asked the Union government for help. The Union agreed to let Judah's company build the railroad from California to the East. Another company, the Union Pacific, would build from the East to California.

survey
(sər-vā´)
to measure land or natural features such as a mountain or lake

invest
(ĭn-vĕst´)
to give money, hoping to get more money back in the future

[?] Many people thought Theodore Judah was crazy. Why did people feel this way about Judah?

Summary continues on next page

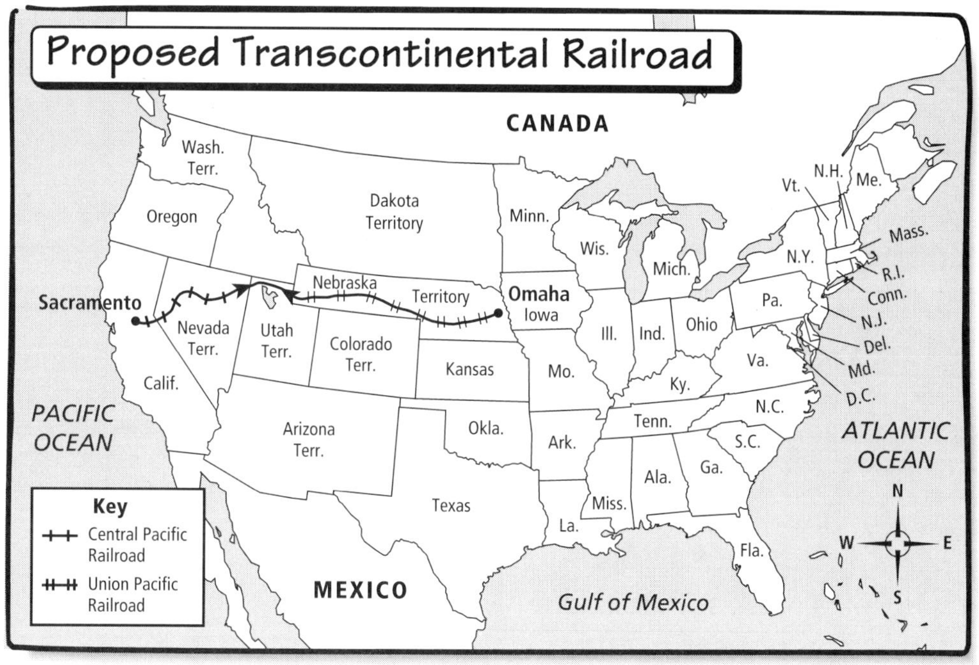

Pushing Judah Out

Judah and the Big Four disagreed about how to build the railroad. Judah wanted to build carefully, whatever the cost. The Big Four did not want to spend that much money. They began to hold secret meetings without Judah. They wanted to force him out of the company.

Judah decided to go to New York. He hoped to find people who would help him buy back the Central Pacific from the Big Four. But crossing the Isthmus of Panama, Judah got sick and died.

Now the Big Four could build the railroad the way they pleased. They turned the Central Pacific into a big business. In a few years, they were very rich and very powerful. But as their power grew, they became unpopular in California.

[?] Based on what you know about Theodore Judah, do you think he would have found some way to buy back the Central Pacific from the Big Four?

Name: Date:

CHAPTER 7

Lesson 3 Preview

Building the Railroad

(*Oh, California* pp. 173–177)

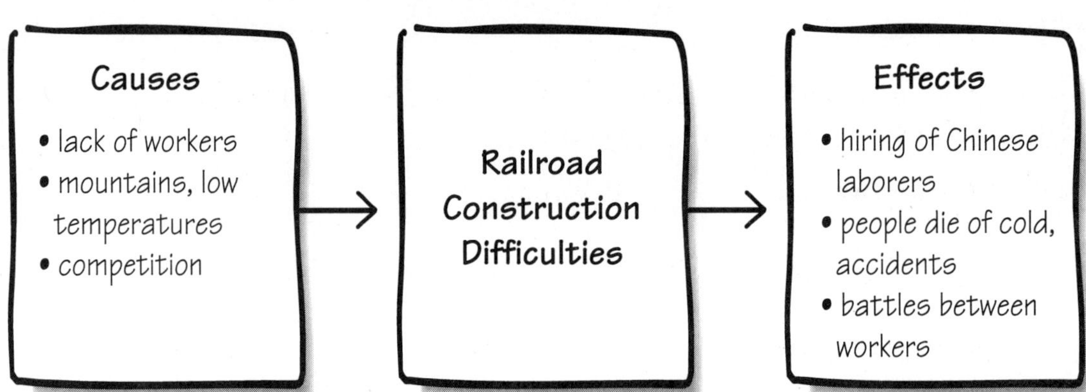

Working on the Railroad
Causes
• lack of workers
• mountains, low temperatures
• competition
Railroad Construction Difficulties
Effects
• hiring of Chinese laborers
• people die of cold, accidents
• battles between workers

1. **Study the graphic overview. Then match the causes in column A to their effects in column B, and write the letter of the answer in the blank.**

Column A	Column B
___ Low, mountain temperatures caused ___.	A. the hiring of Chinese laborers.
___ The competing railroads caused ___.	B. people to die of cold.
___ The lack of workers caused ___.	C. battles between the workers.

2. **Look at the pictures and read the captions in the lesson. Then read the red and blue headings. What problems do you think the railroad will have?**

Name: Date:

CHAPTER 7

Lesson 3 Reading Strategy

Building the Railroad

(*Oh, California* pp. 173–177)

Evaluate This reading strategy helps you recognize the difference between facts and opinions. A fact is something that can be proven to be true. An opinion is a belief based on what a person thinks or feels.

1. Read from the lesson title "Building a Railroad" to the bottom of page 173. Circle the statement below that is a fact.

a. Fights between the railroad crews were the worst battles ever seen.
b. The railroads fought to see who would lay the most track.
c. Blowing up track was more dangerous then rolling boulders onto the track.

2. Read the section "Looking for Workers" on page 175. Circle the statement below that is an opinion.

a. The Central Pacific lost many workers when silver was discovered in Nevada.
b. The Big Four sent people to China to look for more workers.
c. Without Chinese workers, I think the railroad never would have been built.

3. Write a fact about Chinese workers from the text on page 175.

____

4. Read the section "The Great Finish" on pages 176 and 177. Write two facts and two opinions about this section.

Facts	Opinions
1.	1.
2.	2.

C H A P T E R 7

Lesson 3 Summary

Building the Railroad

(*Oh, California* pp. 173–177)

Summary also on Audiotape

Thinking Focus: What were some of the challenges that the builders of the Central Pacific Railroad faced?

Laying the Tracks

For each mile of track a company laid, the United States government gave it valuable land. So each company wanted to lay the most track. As the transcontinental railroad neared its finish, each company raced the other to lay more tracks. Fights broke out between the Central Pacific and the Union Pacific work crews. Union Pacific work crews blew up the track just laid by the Central Pacific. The Central Pacific rolled boulders onto the rails of the Union Pacific.

The Central Pacific workers were used to struggling for every inch of track. Laying the tracks in the Sierra Nevada was hard. During **construction**, workers faced deep snow and bitter cold.

? Think of the pictures you have seen of the Sierra Nevada. Why would it be hard to build a railroad over these mountains?

Looking for Workers

Careful **engineering** was needed to build a railroad through the Sierra Nevada. The Big Four also needed thousands of **laborers,** or workers, to do the job. At first, workers from California did the construction. Then silver was discovered in Nevada. Many workers left for the silver mines. More workers had to be found to finish the railroad.

One of the Big Four, Charles Crocker, had an idea. Why not hire Chinese workers? The Central Pacific hired as many Chinese workers from California as it could find. The Chinese were good workers. So the company sent people to China to find even more workers.

construction
(kən-strŭk′shən)
the work of building something

engineering
(ĕn′jə-nîr′ĭng)
the use of scientific knowledge and rules to build something

laborers
(lā′bər-ərz)
workers

Summary continues on next page

The Chinese took on the hardest and most dangerous jobs. Many froze to death in the cold mountains. Many more died in snow slides or in the explosions used to blast away rocks. Without the Chinese, the railroad might never have crossed the Sierra Nevada.

? How did the Chinese railroad workers help the Central Pacific railroad to finish its job?

The Great Finish

When construction in the Sierra Nevada was complete, workers began to make good progress. It was much easier to lay track on the flatter land beyond the mountains. But workers for the two railroads were still fighting each other. Finally, they agreed to join tracks at a place called Promontory Point in Utah. On May 10, 1868, the two sets of tracks met. A golden spike connected the rails. The job was finished. For California, the transcontinental railroad was a dream come true.

? Why were work crews able to lay the tracks so quickly in Nevada and Utah?

Summary continues on next page

Chapter Overview
Agriculture Advances

Fill in the blank spaces below with information from the chapter.

When:
1870–1890

Where:
Southern California

Who:
Farmers

Farming in California, 1860-1890

More People Arrive
- land for sale
- orange growers
- low railroad fares

More Farming
- new farmers
- ______________
- ______________

Farming Problems
- ______________
- ______________
- land ownership

Name: Date:

CHAPTER 8

Lesson 1 Preview

Farming Takes Hold

(*Oh, California*, pp. 184–187)

Growth of Farming in California
Causes
• technology
• people
• new crops
• refrigeration
Farming begins to grow.
Effect
California develops a productive agriculture industry.

1. Look at the graphic overview above, then read the following word groups. Circle the letter of the word group that names causes for the growth of farming in California.

a. new laws, people, refrigeration, new crops
b. people, new crops, another gold rush, technology
c. refrigeration, people, technology, new crops
d. another gold rush, refrigeration, new crops, people

2. Look at the maps on page 187 in your text and read the title. Between what years do the maps show the growth of farming in California?

____

____

How do the maps show this growth?

____

____

____

____

____

____

____

Name: Date:

CHAPTER 8

Lesson 1 Reading Strategy

Farming Takes Hold

(*Oh, California* pp. 184–187)

Cause and Effect This reading strategy helps you understand events and why they occur. As you read, think about the factors that cause an event. Then think about what the effects of that event may be.

1. **Read the section "Changes in Land Use" on page 185. Circle the letter of the sentence that tells what caused the Chinese to plant vegetable gardens by their mining claims.**
   a. The Chinese had had mostly bad luck mining for gold.
   b. The Chinese realized the miners coming to California needed food.
   c. The Chinese loved fresh vegetables with their meals.

2. **What was the effect of the Chinese selling food?**
   a. Many quit mining when they learned they could make more money farming.
   b. Many found gold while digging in their vegetable gardens.
   c. Many carried vegetables in baskets hanging from poles balanced on their shoulders.

3. **Read the section "The Growth of Wheat" on pages 185 and 186. What caused many farmers in the Central Valley to grow wheat?**

   ____

4. **Read the section "The Move to New Crops" on pages 186 and 187. Then fill in the chart below.**

Cause	Effect
Wheat production dropped.	
People like Ah Bing and Luther Burbank developed better fruits and vegetables.	
	In the 1870s, much of the food was canned before it was shipped.
	In 1888, people across the country began enjoying fresh fruits and vegetables.

CHAPTER 8

Lesson 1 Summary

Farming Takes Hold

(*Oh, California* pp. 184–187)

Summary also on Audiotape

Thinking Focus: How did California's agriculture change in the years following the gold rush?

Changes in Land Use

Long before the gold rush, the Indians and the Spanish grew crops and raised cattle. With the gold rush came more people and the need for more food. The Chinese were the first to realize this. They planted gardens and sold their vegetables. Many left mining to become farmers.

? Explain why there was such a need for the food that Chinese gardeners grew.

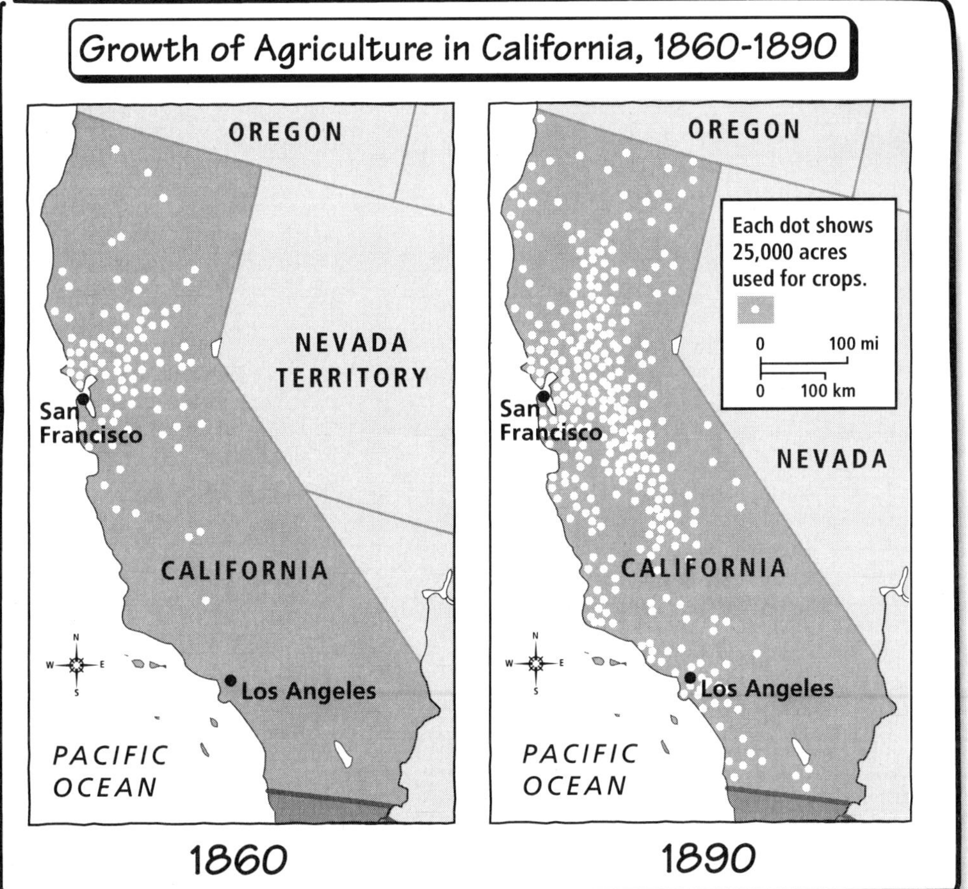

Summary continues on next page

The Growth of Wheat

By the 1860s, thousands of new farmers had settled in California. They grew food for California, the rest of the country, and the world. Wheat was the favorite crop, and California's Central Valley was the perfect place to grow it. The land was flat and easy to plow. The soil was rich. The dry summer heat ripened the wheat. The wheat was so good, it became known around the world.

Each year, California farmers grew more wheat. To plow the huge fields, they joined together many small plows to make a giant plow called a gang plow. Wheat helped these farmers grow rich, but it harmed the soil. Planting the same crop each year used up minerals in the soil that growing wheat needed. As wheat **production** dropped, farmers began looking for new crops to grow.

[?] Give three reasons why the Central Valley was perfect for wheat farming.

The Move to New Crops

Many California farmers began growing fruits and vegetables instead of wheat. Soon farmers became successful growing these new crops. Part of their success was due to people like Ah Bing, a Chinese immigrant who developed the sweet-tasting Bing cherry. Another Californian, Luther Burbank, conducted **experiments** with seeds. He developed fruits and vegetables that tasted better and lasted longer.

In the 1870s, California's fruits and vegetables were transported across the country on trains. Much of the food was canned to keep it fresh for the long trip. Then in 1888, railroads began to use **refrigeration** to keep the food from spoiling. The ice in the refrigerated boxcars kept the food cold and fresh. Now people across the country could enjoy fresh fruits and vegetables from California.

[?] Give two important reasons for the growth of California fruit and vegetable farming.

production
(prə-dŭc'shən)
the total amount made or grown

experiment
(ĭk-spĕr'ə-mənt)
a test done to learn something new

refrigeration
(rĭ-frĭj'ə-rā'shən)
the use of cold air or ice to keep food fresh

Name: Date:

CHAPTER 8

Lesson 2 Preview

Growth in Southern California

(*Oh, California* pp. 190–193)

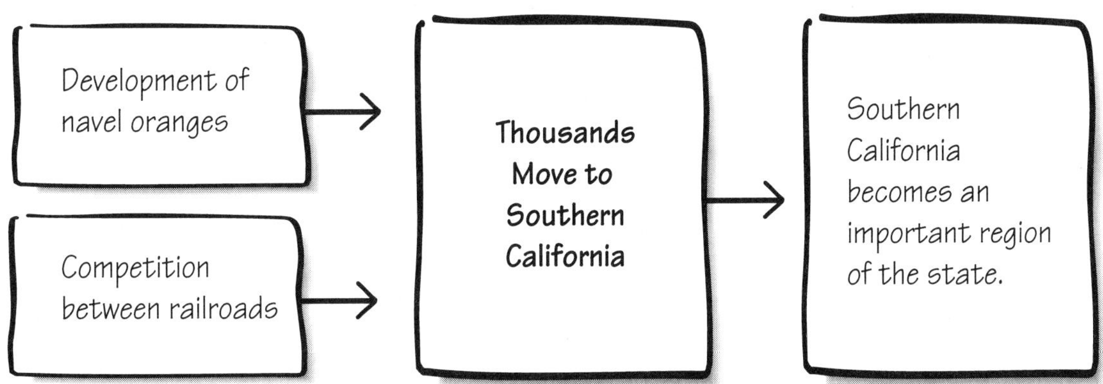

1. Read the graphic overview above. Use it to complete the sentences below.

a. One reason southern California grew as an area in the late 1800s was because of competition between ______________________.

b. Another reason for growth in southern California was the development of ______________________ oranges.

2. Look at the map on page 193 to complete the sentence below.

In 1885, the Santa Fe Railroad competed with the ______________________ in southern California.

Name: Date:

CHAPTER 8

Lesson 2 Reading Strategy

Growth in Southern California

(*Oh, California* pp. 190–193)

Self-Question This reading strategy helps you stay focused on what you read. Ask yourself questions before you read a section. Then read to see if you can find the answer to your questions.

1. **Look at the poster on page 190 and read the caption. Check the question you think the paragraphs on this page would answer.**

   ___ What kinds of vegetables are grown in California?

   ___ How did posters bring people to southern California?

   ___ What was the gold rush?

2. **Read the heading "Southern California's Oranges" on page 191. Write a question you think this section would answer.**

   ____

3. **Look at the picture on page 191 and read the caption. Then read the heading "Railroads and Growth." Write a question you think this section might answer.**

   ____

4. **Look at the map on page 193. What two questions could you ask that this map could answer? Write your questions and answers in the chart below.**

My Questions	My Answers
1.	1.
2.	2.

CHAPTER 8

Lesson 2 Summary

Growth in Southern California

(*Oh, California* pp. 190–193)

Summary also on Audiotape

Thinking Focus: What are two important reasons for the growth of southern California?

Southern California Oranges

At first the oranges grown in southern California were dry, seedy, and sour. So the orange **industry**—the business of growing and selling oranges—was small. Then, thanks to Luther Tibbets, the orange industry took a giant step forward.

In 1873, Tibbets planted two small orange trees that had come from Brazil, a country in South America. Luther's wife, Eliza Tibbets, took good care of the trees. They grew well and produced a special orange called a navel orange. Navel oranges tasted delicious. They were juicy, seedless, and sweet. By 1900, farmers were growing millions of navel oranges in southern California. The orange industry became a huge business.

industry
(ĭn'də-strē)
making goods, growing crops, or producing goods to sell

competition
(kŏm'pĭ-tĭsh'ən)
when two or more companies work against each other to win the most customers

? Give one possible reason for the success of the navel orange besides its good flavor.

Railroads and Growth

Oranges were one reason for southern California growth. Railroads were another.

In the 1870s, business was good for the Southern Pacific Railroad. Its rates were high, but people paid what the railroad charged. There was no other railroad they could use.

Then in 1885 the Sante Fe Railroad opened for business. It began competing with Southern Pacific for customers. To attract riders, the railroads lowered their prices. This **competition** caused a period of fast growth. In 1887 alone, 200,000 people

Summary continues on next page

came to southern California. Some people bought land and became farmers. Others took jobs in growing cities like Los Angeles. Southern California was in a **boom,** just like the one in northern California during the gold rush.

boom
(bōōm)
a sudden time of fast growth or activity

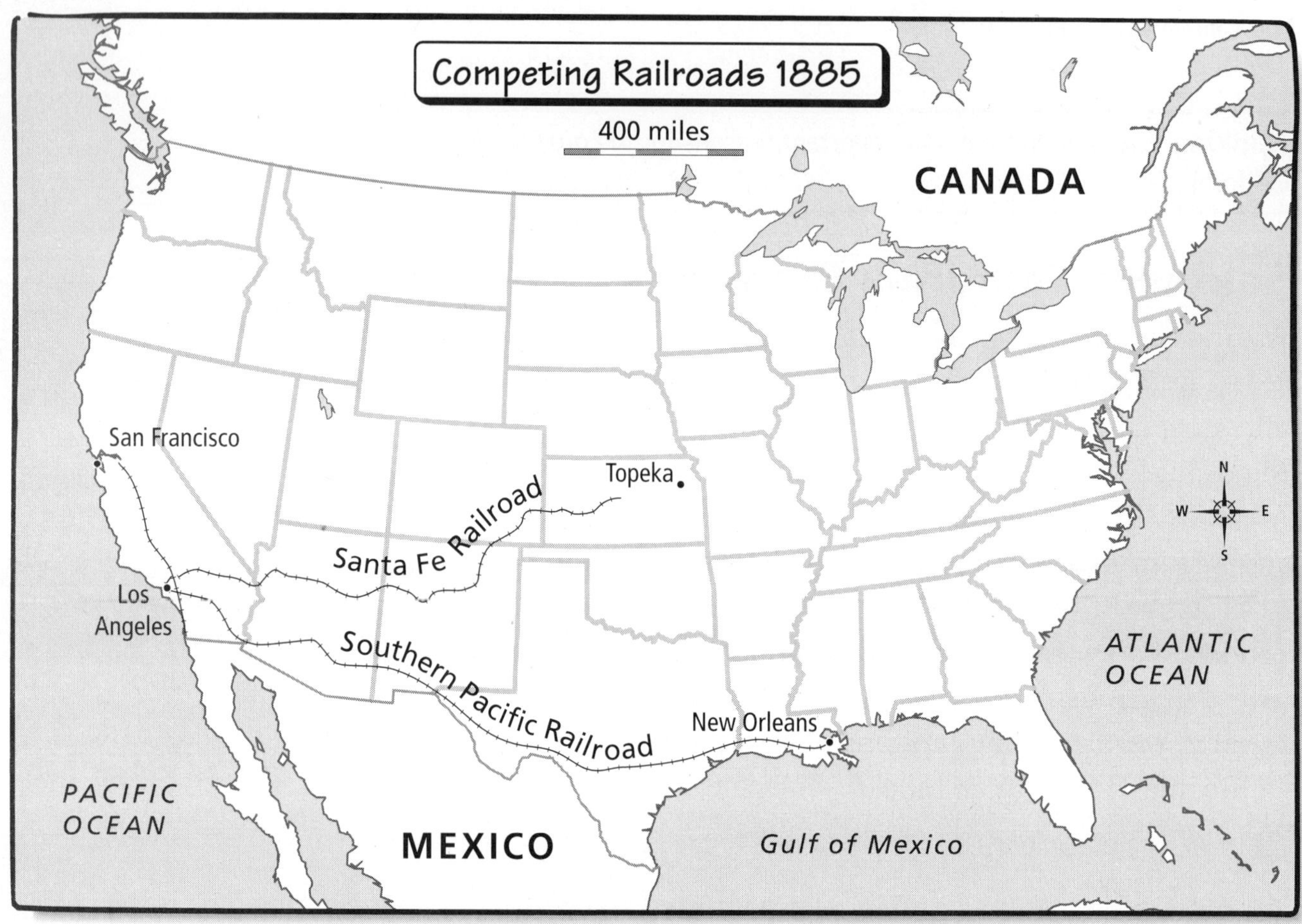

? Give two reasons why railroad competition might have helped southern California grow.

Name: Date:

CHAPTER 8

Lesson 3 Preview

Problems Facing Agriculture

(*Oh, California* pp. 195–199)

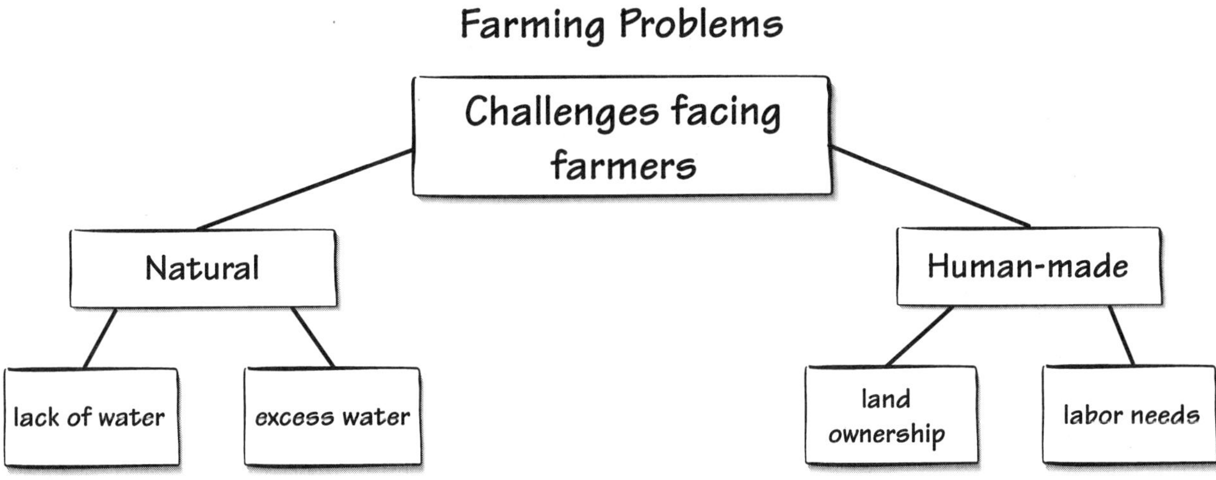

1. Study the graphic overview to answer the question. What two kinds of problems faced California's farmers in the late 1800s?

____

____

2. Look at the pictures on the pages listed below. Write the best title for each picture. Choose from these titles.

Orange Trees	Farm Workers
Water for the Fields	Giant Plows

a. page 195 ______________

b. page 196 ______________

Name: Date:

CHAPTER 8

Lesson 3 Reading Strategy

Problems Facing Agriculture

(*Oh, California* pp. 195–199)

Compare and Contrast This reading strategy helps you understand how events are similar and different. As you read about historical events, think about how they compare and contrast with events you already know.

1. **Read the section "Water Problems" on pages 196–197. Fill in the chart to tell about the different water problems some California farmers had.**

Not Enough Water	Too Much Water

2. **Name one way in which the problems were similar.**

3. **Name the ways in which farmers solved their water problems.**

4. **Read the section "Land Problems" on pages 197–198. Name one way in which the problems of the Mussel Slough farmers were like those of other farmers and one way in which they were different.**

   Same:

   Different:

5. **Read the section "Patterns for the Future" on page 198. Name one way in which tenant farmers were like migrant workers and one way in which they were different.**

   Same:

   Different:

CHAPTER 8

Lesson 3 Summary

Problems Facing Agriculture

(*Oh, California* pp. 195–199)

Summary also on Audiotape

Thinking Focus: What were some of the challenges that faced California's farmers in the second half of the 1800s?

Water Problems

In many parts of California there is not enough summer rain for growing crops. During the 1800s farmers dug trenches to bring water from nearby rivers to their fields. Even today, most of California's farms depend on **irrigation.** But irrigation systems are expensive to build. Sometimes farmers join together to share the cost. Other farmers buy land that is already irrigated.

Water caused different problems in other parts of California. Spring rains brought floods that ruined the crops. Along the Sacramento River, farmers built **levees,** or high ridges, to hold back the water.

irrigation
(ĭr′ĭ-gā′shən)
the use of trenches and canals to bring water to dry land

levee
(lĕv′ē)
a piece of land built up along a riverbank to keep flood waters from overflowing

[?] Explain two ways that water can create problems for farmers.

Land Problems

In the 1870s, Southern Pacific Railroad owned much of the farmland in California. In order to make money, the railroad decided to sell some of its land. This land included Mussel Slough, located in the Central Valley. The railroad agreed to sell Mussel Slough to farmers for five dollars an acre. Before the sale was complete, the railroad let the farmers use the land. The farmers planted crops and built an irrigation system.

When Southern Pacific realized that the farmers' work had made the land more valuable, they broke their promise to sell Mussel Slough to the farmers. Instead, they sold it to two men for 25 dollars an acre. When the men tried to move onto the land, the farmers fought back. Five people were killed in the fight. In the end, the railroad drove the farmers off the land.

Summary continues on next page

Frank Norris wrote a book called *The Octopus* about the problem of fighting the railroad. A character says, "I could have told you how little chance you had. When will you people realize that you can't buck against the railroad? . . . it's like me going out in a paper boat and shooting peas at a battleship."

[?] Based on the words you just read, do you think the book *The Octopus* is for or against the railroad? Explain your answer.

Patterns for the Future

In the late 1800s, most of California's farmland was owned by rich people or big companies like Southern Pacific Railroad. **Migrant laborers** did most of the work on these large farms. They moved from farm to farm picking crops. Their lives were very hard because they worked for long hours under the hot sun for very little pay. Other farmers were **tenant** farmers.

Today, California farms feed people throughout the United States and around the world. Some farms are owned by large companies. Much of the work on these farms is still done by migrant workers who work long hours for low pay.

[?] Why is much of the work on California's farms done by migrant laborers?

migrant laborer
(mī′grənt lā′bər-ər)
farm worker who move from farm to farm picking ripe crops

tenant
(tĕn′ənt)
a person who pays rent to use land that belongs to someone else

Chapter Overview
A Mix of Cultures

Fill in the blank spaces below with information from the chapter.

When:
1850-1920
Where:
California's cities and towns
Who:
immigrants from Europe and Asia

Mixing of Cultures

The New Californias 1850–1920

- African Americans from the ______________
- people from ______________
- people from ______________

Problems for the New Californians

- unfair ______________
- unfair ______________
- unfair ______________

Pride in New Californians

- enriching California
- ______________ people
- ______________ people

Name: ______________________ Date: ______________________

CHAPTER 9

Lesson 1 Preview

The New Californians

(*Oh, California* pp. 204–208)

1. **Study the graphic overview above to answer the following question: Why did new immigrants move to California?**

   a. ______________________________

   b. ______________________________

2. **Look at the map on page 207 in your text. Find the town that is closest to where you live and write its name here.**

   ____

   What immigrant group(s) helped to settle this town?

   ____

Name: Date:

CHAPTER 9

Lesson 1 Reading Strategy

The New Californians

(*Oh, California* pp. 204–208)

Think About Words This reading strategy helps you figure out the meaning of new words. When you come to an unfamiliar word, look for word parts you already know and use clues such as context and pictures.

1.–2. Read the first four paragraphs of the lesson, up to the heading "Why California?" on page 204. Then read this sentence: Joseph Griffen *unearthed* a metal box. What does *unearthed* mean?

____

Name two clues from your reading that could help you understand what *unearthed* means.

____

____

3.–4. Read "Immigrants from Asia" on pages 205–208. Fill in as much of the chart as you can to help you figure out what the heading word *arrivals* means.

WORD: arrivals

Clues from the reading:

Clues from the pictures:

Similar words I already know:

Parts of words I already know:

The word means:

CHAPTER 9

Lesson 1 Summary

The New Californians

(*Oh, California* pp. 204–208)

Summary also on Audiotape

Thinking Focus: Who are immigrants, and why did they come to California?

Why California?

From 1890 to the 1920s, about 35,000 African Americans moved to western states like California. They left the South to escape drought and crop failure. But they also left to escape unfair laws. These laws forced them to live separately from white Americans, attend separate schools, and accept low-paying jobs. Sadly, African Americans still faced much of the same unfair treatment in California as they had in the South.

In the United States, people often move to find better lives. This is also true of **immigrants**, people who move to another country. Thousands of immigrants came to California in the late 1800s and early 1900s. They believed California was a place to find wealth and to make their dreams of a better life come true.

immigrant
(ĭm′ĭ-grənt)
a person who moves to another country, usually to find a better life

Immigrants Came to California to...

start farms or work on farms

work on the transcontinental railroad

look for gold

? Why did people want to move to California?

Summary continues on next page

Immigrants from Europe

Many immigrants from Europe first settled in the East. Hagop and Garabed Seropian, for example, moved to Massachusetts. They came from Armenia to escape the violence that was happening there. Then in 1881, they moved to California where the weather was better for Hagop's health.

Other European immigrants came to California because they were unhappy in the East. They were often treated cruelly by people who did not want outsiders taking their jobs. They brought their customs and way of life to California.

? What was life like for many European immigrants when they first settled in the United States?

Immigrants from Asia

Many immigrants crossed the Pacific Ocean to get to California. Many of them knew nothing about life in the United States. So when they entered California, they found unfamiliar people and cultures.

The first Asian immigrants were from China. Many came during the gold rush. Others came to build the transcontinental railroad. By the end of the 1880s, many Japanese immigrants had moved to California. Philippine workers came during the late 1920s to work on California farms. All of these immigrants came looking for a better life. Some found it. Others did not.

? What experiences did immigrants from Europe and Asia have in common?

Name: Date:

CHAPTER 9

Lesson 2 Preview

Conflicts Between Cultures

(*Oh, California* pp. 209–213)

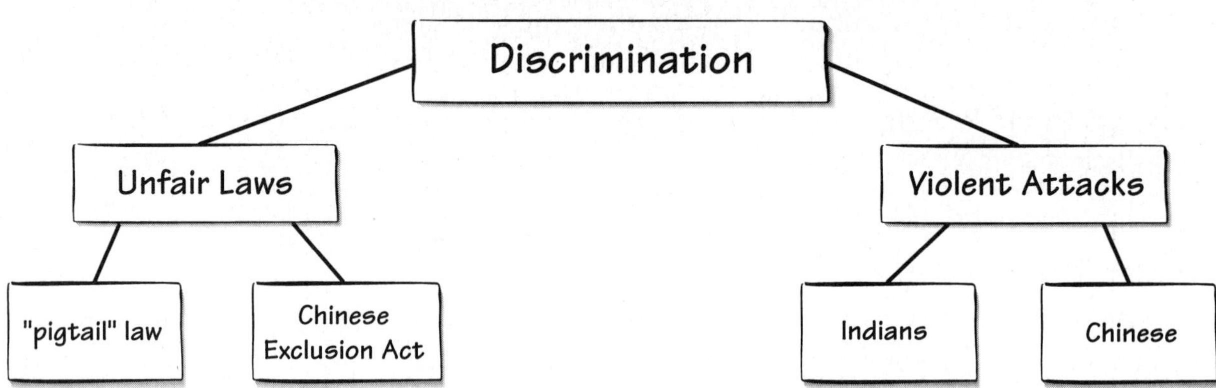

1. Read the graphic overview above. Use words from the graphic overview to complete the sentences below.

a. Due to discrimination, there were terrible attacks against the ____________ and the ____________ living in California.

b. Two examples of California's unfair laws against Asian immigrants are the ____________ and the ____________.

2. Look at the graph titled Chinese Population in California on page 211. How does the graph show that the Chinese Exclusion Act affected the population of Chinese in California?

____

____

____

Name: Date:

CHAPTER 9

Lesson 2 Reading Strategy

Conflicts Between Cultures

(*Oh, California* pp. 209–213)

Predict/Infer This reading strategy helps you understand what you have read and what you will read next. Before you read a section, think about the titles, pictures, and captions. Then think about what will happen in the selection.

1. **Look at the pictures on pages 209–213. Then read the lesson headings. What do you predict will be the problem described in this lesson? Check your answer.**

   ___ the unfair treatment of Californians

   ___ the unfair treatment of Asians

   ___ the unfair treatment of school children

2. **Name two clues that helped you make your prediction.**

   ____

3. **Read the heading "More Discrimination" on page 211 and look at the graph. What do you predict will happen to California's Chinese population?**

   ____

4. **How did your knowledge of discrimination and the graph help you to make your prediction?**

   ____

5. **Read the heading "Immigrants Struggle" on page 212. Read the first paragraph under the heading. Then fill in the chart below.**

What I Know	What I Predict

CHAPTER 9

Lesson 2 Summary

Conflicts Between Cultures

(*Oh, California* pp. 209–213)

Summary also on Audiotape

Thinking Focus: How have immigrants been treated in California and how have they responded?

Unfair Treatment

Many immigrants in California faced unfair treatment, or **discrimination.** People often discriminated against immigrants because they felt they were better than the newcomers. For example, the Chinese did not dress, talk, or wear their hair the way other Californians did. So other people singled them out for cruel treatment. Immigrants also faced racism. Racism is when a group of people judge others mostly on the basis of skin color.

California Indians faced discrimination and racism. Early settlers mistreated the Indians. They took their land and often their lives. Many more Indians died on **reservations**, small areas of land that the United States government set aside for them. The land was so poor the Indians could not get enough food to eat. By the early 1900s, hunger, disease, and violence had wiped out most of California's Indians.

discrimination
(dĭ-skrĭm´ə-nā´shən)
unfair treatment of a group of people because of their differences in language, appearance, or way of life

reservation
(rĕz´ər-vā´shən)
land set aside by the United States government for Native Americans

? Explain why the number of Indians in California started to fall in the mid-1800s.

Summary continues on next page

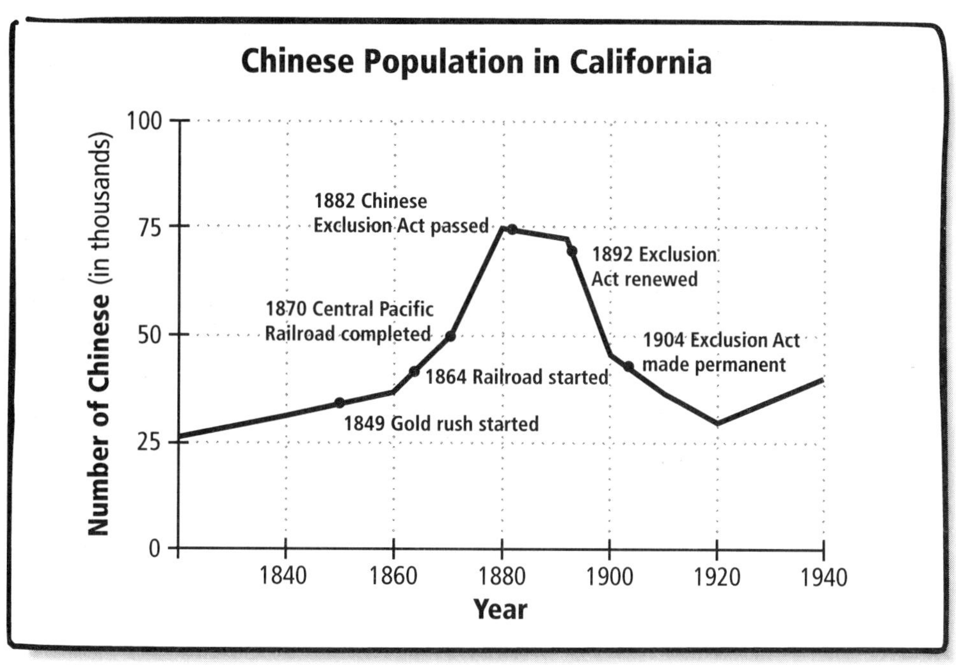

More Discrimination

During the 1880s, the U.S. government passed laws to keep Asians out of the country. The Chinese Exclusion Act of 1882 did not allow Chinese immigration for 10 years. The Exclusion Act was later extended and made permanent. Asians had to pass through Angel Island in San Francisco Bay and answer questions about their reasons for coming to California. During this time, they were kept like prisoners in crowded buildings. Some were never allowed to enter the United States.

? What were two ways that Asians in California suffered from discrimination?

Immigrants Struggle

Immigrants often settled together so they could make each other feel at home. Many Chinese and other immigrants held onto their customs and traditions. They made their neighborhoods look like those in China. They also celebrated special holidays. Celebrating together helped immigrants forget the discrimination they faced from other Americans.

? What did immigrants do to adjust to life in California?

Name: Date:

CHAPTER 9

Lesson 3 Preview

Contributing to California

(*Oh, California* pp. 214–217)

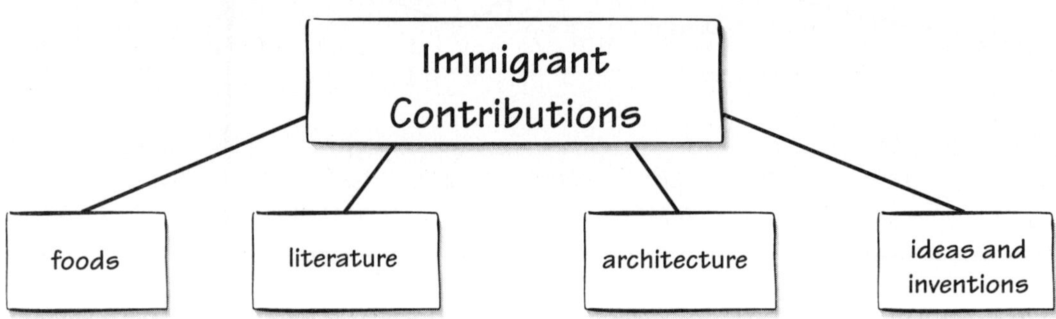

1. **Read the graphic overview above. Then write a word from the graphic that best describes each group of words below.**

   a. ____________________ newspaper, novel about unfair treatment

   b. ____________________ chocolate candy, sourdough bread

   c. ____________________ new kind of transportation

   d. ____________________ Japanese home and garden

2. **Look at the picture of Ng Poon Chew on page 217 and read the caption. In your own words, tell how Ng contributed to California.**

____

____

____

____

Name: Date:

CHAPTER 9

Lesson 3 Reading Strategy

Contributing to California

(*Oh, California* pp. 214–217)

Finding the Main Idea This reading strategy helps you organize and remember what you read. When you finish a selection, jot down the main idea and its supporting details.

1. **Read the first two paragraphs on page 214. Then read the section "Colorful California" on pages 214–215. Write *M* by the sentence that best tells the main idea of the section.**
   ___ An ethnic group is a group of people who come from the same nation or culture.
   ___ Ghirardelli's chocolate factory still stands today.
   ___ Immigrants have given many things to California.

2. **Read the section "Maria Amparo Ruiz de Burton" on pages 215–216. Write *M* by the sentence that best tells the main idea of this section.**
   ___ Ruiz de Burton was a Californio.
   ___ Ruiz de Burton wrote about the unfair treatment of the Californios.
   ___ Ruiz de Burton used a false name when she wrote her book.

3. **Read the section "Ng Poon Chew" on page 217. Then fill in the chart below.**

Main Idea	Supporting Details

CHAPTER 9

Lesson 3 Summary

Contributing to California

(*Oh, California* pp. 214–217)

Summary also on Audiotape

Thinking Focus: How have California's immigrants contributed to the state?

Colorful California

Domingo Ghirardelli left Italy and moved to California. He hoped to get rich mining gold. When he did not find gold, Ghirardelli came up with another idea—making chocolates and candies for the miners. By 1851, business was booming. Ghirardelli had to build a big factory in San Francisco. Today, the building is a city **landmark.**

California's immigrants have made contributions throughout the state. Many of its farms and ranches were built with the help of immigrants. Many of California's foods and place names came from immigrants or ethnic groups. Even some of California's holidays and festivals were introduced by **ethnic groups.** From factory owners to migrant workers, all immigrants have played a part in making California a state of many nations.

[?] Must a person be famous to contribute to his or her community? Why or why not?

landmark
(lănd′märk′)
an important place or spot in a community

ethnic group
(ĕth′nĭk gro͞op)
a group of people who share common background, race, or religion

Summary continues on next page

Gifts of Ideas

Some people contribute by sharing ideas. Maria Amparo Ruiz de Burton belonged to an ethnic group, the Californios. In 1885, she wrote *The Squatter and the Don.* This book told about the end of the Californios' way of life and how they unfairly lost their ranchos. At that time, women writers had trouble getting their books printed. So Ruiz de Burton used a false name to publish her book. Today, people know the story of the Californios because of her book.

Ng Poon Chew, a Chinese immigrant, also wanted to share his ideas. He started a newspaper called the *Chinese American Daily Paper.* Here, Chinese readers could share their thoughts and ideas. Ng also used the paper to fight for the rights of the Chinese. Ng traveled around the United States speaking against discrimination.

[?] What ideas did Maria Amparo Ruiz de Burton and Ng Poon Chew contribute to California?

Summary continues on next page

Chapter Overview
Building a Better California

Fill in the blank spaces below with information from the chapter.

When:
1895–1940

Where:
Los Angeles,
Hollywood,
San Francisco,
San Joaquin Valley

Growth and Change for California

- **1890s** Oil discoveries are made in southern California.
- **1906** ____________________
- **1910** The Progressive's candidate, Hiram Johnson, becomes governor.
- **1911** ____________________
- **1913** ____________________
- **1914** The San Pedro harbor makes Los Angeles an important port city. The Panama Canal cuts travel time from the East to one month.
- **1915** Film industry begins to grow with the first silent movies.
- **1917** ____________________
- **1929** Great Depression begins. People seek new lives in California.
- **1930s** Dust Bowl families come to California to find work.
- **1933** President Roosevelt's New Deal program brings hope to the people.
- **1937** ____________________

Name: ______________________ Date: ______________

CHAPTER 10

Lesson 1 Preview

Growth of Industry

(*Oh, California* pp. 226–230)

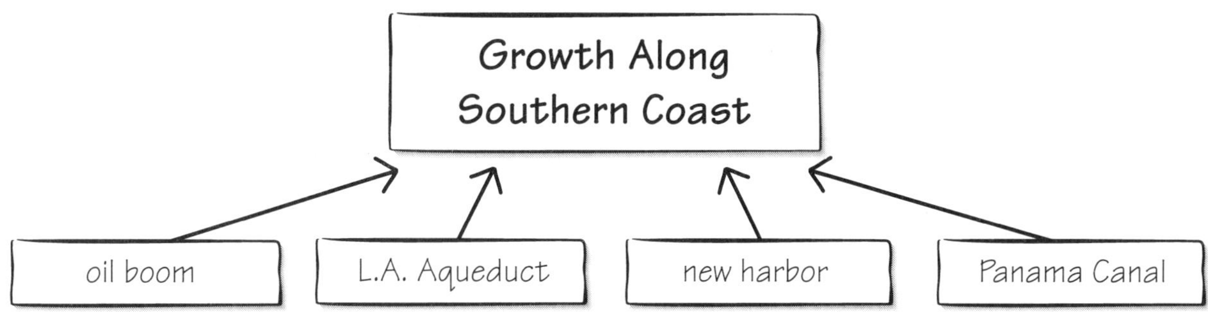

1. **Study the graphic overview above. Use words from the graphic overview to complete these sentences.**

   a. Two projects that greatly affected shipping in southern California were the ______________________ and the ______________________.

   b. The discovery of the natural resource ______________________ led to new growth in southern California.

   c. The ______________________ brought badly needed water from the eastern part of California to Los Angeles.

2. **Look at the photograph on page 227 in your text and read the sign on the truck. What do you think a horseless carriage is?**

   ____

   ____

   Why would a horseless carriage use oil?

   ____

   ____

   ____

   ____

Name: ______________________ Date: ______________________

CHAPTER 10

Lesson 1 Reading Strategy

Growth of Industry

(*Oh, California* pp. 226–230)

Sequence This reading strategy helps you follow what is happening in your reading. As you read, pay attention to dates and times, as well as to words such as *before, finally, after,* and *then*.

1. **Read the first two paragraphs under "Oil Booms in California." Then place the following events in order by writing 1, 2, and 3 in the blanks.**

   ___ Charlie Woods hits a gusher near the San Joaquin Valley.

   ___ The Chumash Indians use oil to seal their canoes.

   ___ New machines and industries needing oil cause an oil boom in California.

2. **Read the paragraphs under "New Uses of 'Black Gold'." Check the event that came first in each pair.**

   a. ___ Trains run on diesel oil. ___ Trains run on coal.

   b. ___ Farms use horses and plows. ___ Farms use tractors.

3. **Read the first paragraph under "Growth Brings Water Problems" on page 228. What words help you understand the sequence of events?**

   ____

4. **Read "A Closer Look" on page 229 and from the head "New Projects Boost Trade" to the end of the lesson. Complete the timeline below with the dates and events.**

1899	______	1914
Work begins on ______ Harbor	Los Angeles Aqueduct brings water from ______	San Pedro Harbor opens; The ______ Canal opens.

CHAPTER 10

Lesson 1 Summary

Growth of Industry

(*Oh, California* pp. 226–230)

Summary also on Audiotape

Thinking Focus: How did four big events help California's southern coast grow in the early 1900s?

Oil Booms in California

Long ago, the Chumash Indians had used oil to seal their canoes. Californios had used it to seal roofs for their adobe homes. By the early 1900s, there were many new uses for oil because the nation's growing industries used machines that needed oil. Oil became so valuable, it was called "black gold."

Drillers discovered oil up and down the California coast. The biggest oil strikes were along the southern coast of the state. The oil boom brought new growth to these areas.

Fuel can be made from oil. Trains once ran by burning coal that made a cloud of thick, black smoke. But diesel fuel made from oil was cleaner and easier to use. Tractors also ran on diesel fuel. As oil became plentiful, tractors replaced the horses and plows on farms. Another oil user was the automobile. It ran on a type of fuel called gasoline.

[?] Why did oil become so valuable in California?

Growth Brings Water Problems

The oil boom brought more people and industries to California. This growth created a new problem. Los Angeles was running out of water. So city officials decided to bring water from the Owens River to the city.

Summary continues on next page

The river was 250 miles away from Los Angeles, across a desert and tall mountains. An **aqueduct** was built to carry the water to the city. It was one of the biggest engineering projects in the country's history. But when it was finished Los Angeles had enough water.

aqueduct
(ăk′wĭ-dŭkt′)
a giant water pipe

canal
(kə-năl′)
a waterway built to join one body of water to another

[?] What problems did Los Angeles face in meeting its water needs?

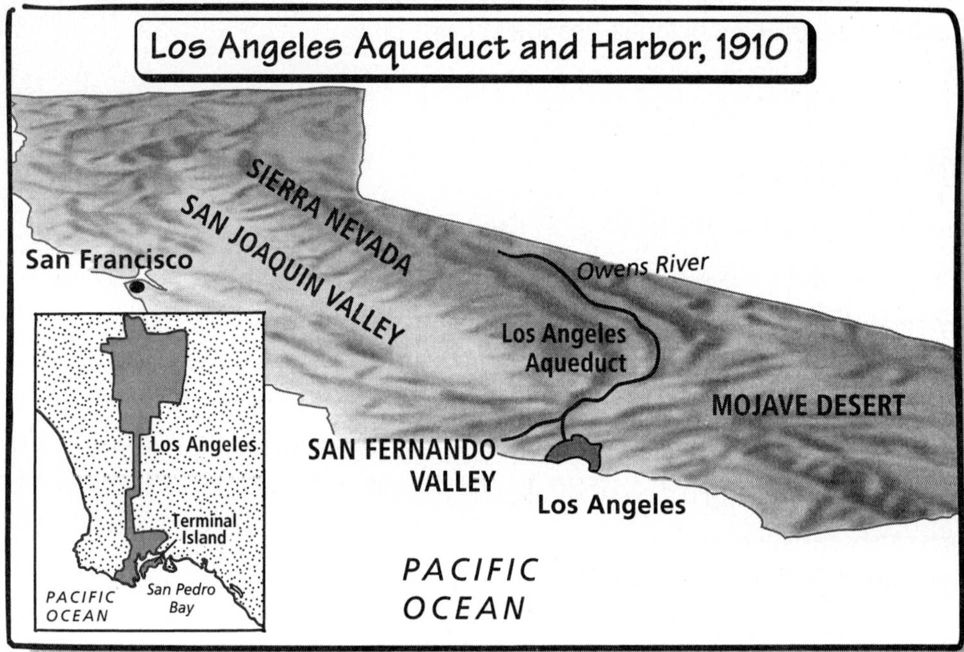

New Projects Boost Trade

Two more projects made Los Angeles grow. One was the building of the San Pedro Harbor. A harbor is a protected body of water deep enough for ships to dock in. San Francisco had a natural harbor. But Los Angeles had to dig a harbor. The new harbor made Los Angeles a major port.

At the same time, a new transportation link opened in Panama. There, the United States built a 51-mile-long **canal** to connect the Pacific and Atlantic oceans. Now ships carrying California goods could travel to the East Coast in only one month.

[?] How did the construction of San Pedro Harbor and the Panama Canal help Los Angeles?

Name: Date:

CHAPTER 10

Lesson 2 Preview

Progress for People

(*Oh, California* pp. 232–235)

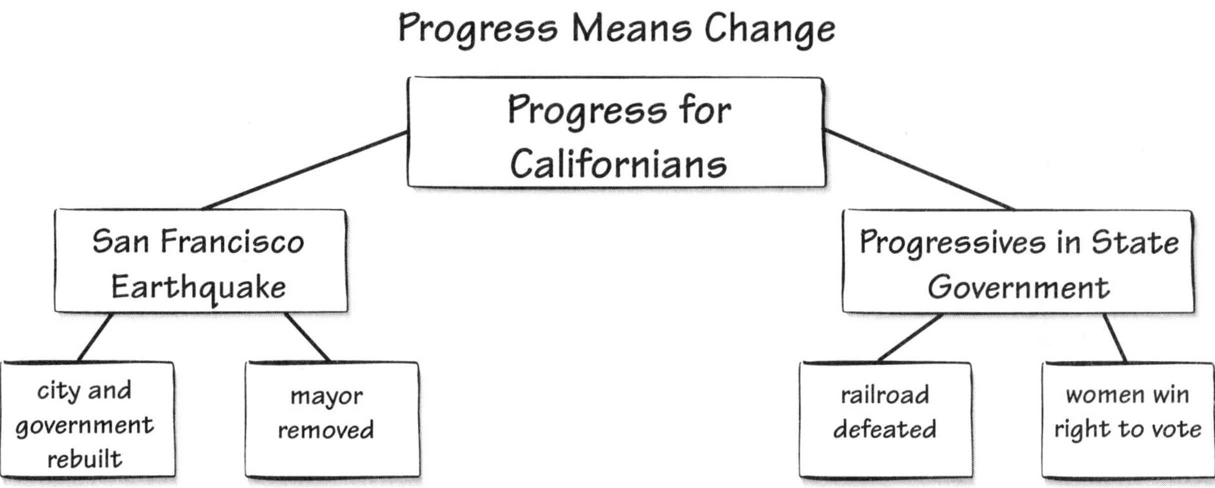

1. Look at the graphic overview above. Then answer the questions.

a. What disaster gave Californians a chance to make changes in their communities?

____

b. What political group helped women get the right to vote?

____

2. Look at the picture and read the caption on page 232. What do the picture and caption tell you about the San Francisco earthquake?

____

____

____

____

Name: Date:

CHAPTER 10

Lesson 2 Reading Strategy

Progress for People

(*Oh, California* pp. 232–235)

Think About Words This reading strategy helps you figure out the meaning of new words. When you come to an unfamiliar word, look for word parts you already know and use clues such as context and pictures.

1. **Read the section "Rebuilding the Government" on page 233. Then read this sentence: Business leaders gave bribes to the mayor and other city officials. What is an *official*?**

   ___

2. **Name two clues from your reading that could help you understand what an *official* is.**

   ___

   ___

3. **Read "California Builds a Better Government" on page 234. Which definition best tells what the word *politics* means in this section?**

   ___ the study of government

   ___ the activities of a government

   ___ a person's beliefs

4. **Read the section "Women Bring Change" on pages 234–235. Look at the picture on page 235 and read the caption. Then fill in as much of the chart as you can to figure out what the word *laborer* means.**

WORD: laborer

Clues from the reading: ___

Clues from the pictures: ___

Similar words I already know: ___

Parts of words I already know: ___

The word means: ___

CHAPTER 10

Lesson 2 Summary

Progress for People

(*Oh, California* pp. 232–235)

Thinking Focus: What problems did Californians try to solve in the early 1900s?

San Francisco Cleans Up

On April 18, 1906, a huge earthquake hit San Francisco. Chimneys fell, roofs caved in, and stoves overturned. Fires broke out everywhere. The earthquake also snapped the city's water pipes. Without water to fight the fire, much of San Francisco burned.

After the earthquake, San Franciscans began putting the city back together. Money, food, and workers came from all over the country to help. President Theodore Roosevelt sent army troops and government money. San Francisco's mayor, Eugene Schmitz, moved quickly to set up the rebuilding.

At the same time, San Franciscans decided to rebuild the city's government. For years, the mayor and other city officials had been taking thousands of dollars in **bribes.** These bribes were paid by the men who ran the big gas, telephone, and railroad companies. In return, these companies were allowed to charge high prices. This hurt smaller California businesses who couldn't pay the high prices.

bribe
(brīb)
money offered to persuade someone to act dishonestly

A group of citizens took action to stop companies from giving bribes. Many business people and city officials were brought to trial. In the end, Mayor Schmitz was kicked out of office.

? Why was the city government of San Francisco in need of rebuilding?

Summary continues on next page

California Builds a Better Government

Many Californians thought that big business had grown too powerful. The most hated company was Southern Pacific Railroad. It held power over newspapers and many other businesses. A lawyer named Hiram Johnson decided to fight the railroad.

Johnson was a member of the **Progressives.** Progressives wanted to limit the power of big business and make government more honest. Johnson ran for governor in 1910. If elected, he promised to kick Southern Pacific Railroad out of politics. Johnson won the election and kept his promise. Southern Pacific Railroad had finally been beaten.

Progressives
(prə-grĕs′ĭvz)
a group of people who worked in the early 1900s to better the government and society

? What kind of progress did the Progressives try to bring about?

Women Bring Change

California women saw that many people in the state were suffering. Men, women, and children worked long hours in places like canneries and laundries. Wages were low, and many families went hungry. Housing was crowded and rundown. Food was often unsafe to eat.

In 1910, women in California could not vote and had no say in government. Still, they worked for progress. For example, they wrote articles urging the government to pass laws to protect workers. In 1911, women finally had a say in government. California passed a law that gave women the right to vote.

? How did women bring change to California when they had no say in government?

Name: Date:

CHAPTER 10

Lesson 3 Preview

New Challenges

(*Oh, California* pp. 241–245)

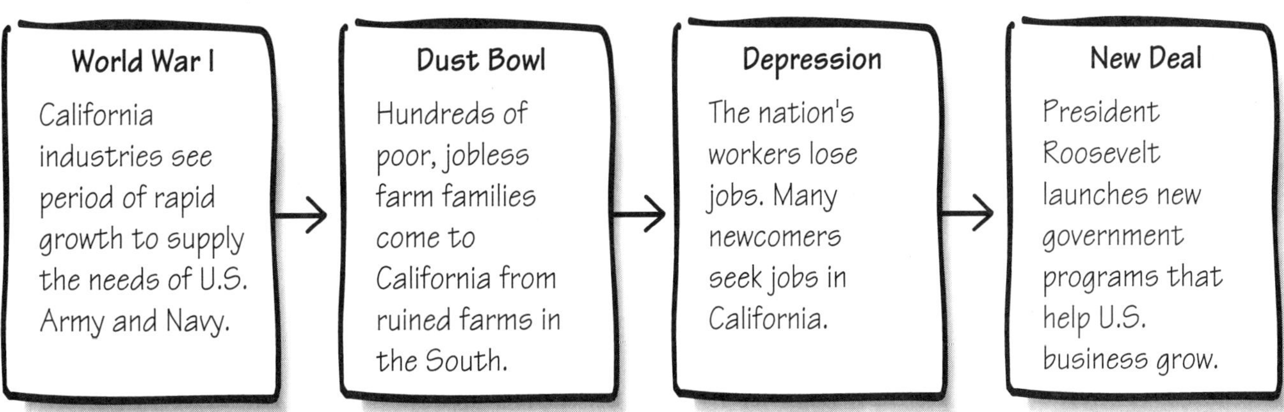

Big Events Challenge Californians
World War I
California industries see period of rapid growth to supply the needs of U.S. Army and Navy.
Dust Bowl
Hundreds of poor, jobless farm families come to California from ruined farms in the South.
Depression
The nation's workers lose jobs. Many newcomers seek jobs in California.
New Deal
President Roosevelt launches new government programs that help U.S. business grow.

1. Look at the graphic overview above. Then answer the questions.

a. What two events brought jobless newcomers to California?

____

____

b. What two events brought a period of growth to California and its industries?

____

____

2. Look at the map on page 243. What states were affected by the Dust Bowl?

____

____

____

Name: Date:

CHAPTER 10

Lesson 3 Reading Strategy

New Challenges

(*Oh, California* pp. 241–245)

Predit/Infer This reading strategy helps you understand what you have read and what you will read next. Before you read a section, think about the titles, pictures, and captions. Then think about what will happen in the selection.

1. **Read page 241 and the headings and the first paragraph on page 242. Then look at the pictures and read the captions. What industry do you predict will be described in this section? Check your answer.**

   ___ the food industry

   ___ the movie industry

   ___ the oil industry

2. **Name the clues that helped you make your prediction.**

   ____

3. **Read the section "Depression and the California Dream" and the first paragraph under the blue head "The Great Depression Hurts Workers" on page 243. Look at the map and read the caption. What do you predict will happen to many families affected by the Dust Bowl and the Great Depression?**

   ___ They will rebuild their farms and businesses.

   ___ They will help build a highway called Route 66.

   ___ They will go to California to start new lives.

4. **Read the first paragraph on page 245 under "Help for the Needy." Read the blue head and the picture caption. Then fill in the chart below.**

What I Know	What I Predict

CHAPTER 10

Lesson 3 Summary

New Challenges

(*Oh, California* pp. 241–245)

Thinking Focus: What events helped and hurt California from 1917 to 1940?

Wartime and Peacetime Growth

In 1917 the United States entered World War I. Even though the war was fought in Europe, times were hard for Americans. Many families lost fathers, brothers, and sons in battle. But war also brought growth. California industries produced food for the troops, cotton for uniforms, oil for war machines, and ships for the navy.

World War I also brought growth to the movie industry. To forget about the war, people went to see movies. Many of these movies were made in Hollywood. The movie business brought visitors to the state. Soon **tourism,** or travel for pleasure, became a big business.

? In what ways did California grow during World War I and afterward?

Depression and the California Dream

During the 1920s, two things happened in the United States that greatly affected California.

- The **Dust Bowl** was a region in the center of the country. The soil had dried out mostly due to lack of rain. The wind blew the soil into huge dust storms that destroyed farms.
- The **Great Depression** was a time when workers all over the country lost their jobs. Many people could not pay their bills or feed their families.

Some families who lost homes and farms because of the Dust Bowl or the Great Depression came to California looking for work. Among them were many Mexicans and Filipinos. Because

tourism
(to͝or′ĭz′əm)
travel for pleasure

Dust Bowl
(dŭst bōl)
a region in the middle of the United States where dust storms raged during the 1920s and 1930s

Great Depression
(grāt dĭ-prĕsh′ən)
from 1929 to 1940, when many workers all over the country lost their jobs

Summary continues on next page

these immigrants usually worked for less pay than white workers, some whites became angry. They claimed that the immigrants stole their jobs. Some Californians wanted to pass laws that would keep immigrants from coming to California.

[?] How did the Dust Bowl and the Great Depression affect California?

Help for the Needy

In 1933 people were still jobless and hungry. Franklin Delano Roosevelt, the new President, came up with a plan called the **New Deal** to put people back to work building roads, dams, canals, bridges, and parks throughout the United States.

California also put thousands of people to work building the Golden Gate Bridge. The bridge stood as a sign of the determination and hard work that would pull the country out of the Great Depression.

New Deal
(no͞o dēl)
the programs created by President Franklin Delano Roosevelt to lift the United States out of the Great Depression

[?] How did the New Deal help California?

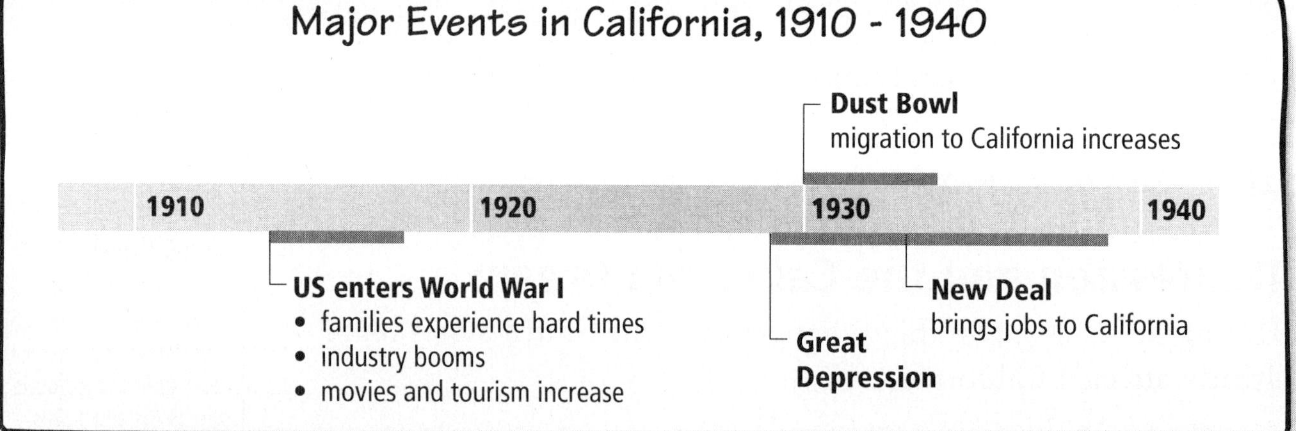

Chapter Overview
World War II and Beyond

Fill in the blank spaces below with information from the chapter.

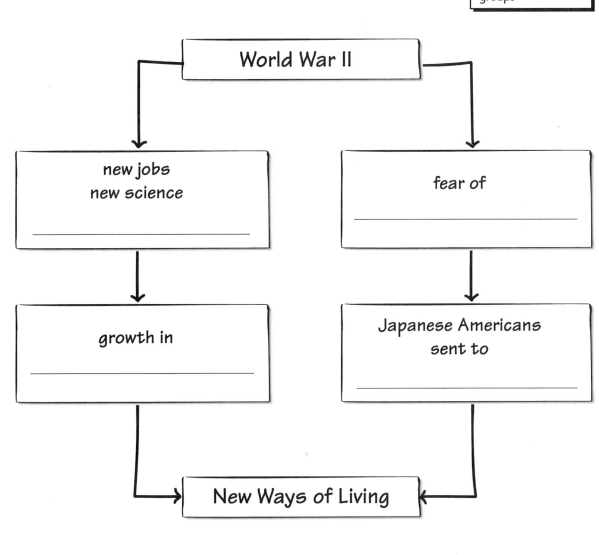

When:
1940–1965

Who:
Japanese Americans, Mexican Americans, African Americans, new immigrant groups

World War II: Tragedy and Growth in California

World War II

new jobs
new science
____

growth in
____

fear of
____

Japanese Americans
sent to
____

New Ways of Living

Name: Date:

CHAPTER 11

Lesson 1 Preview

California in Wartime

(*Oh, California* pp. 250–253)

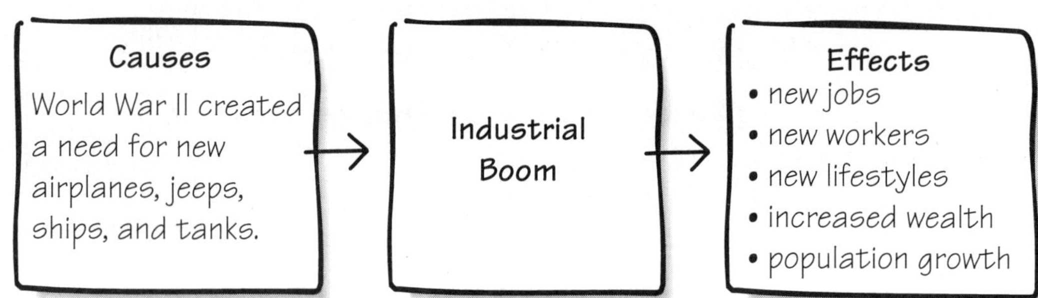

1. **Study the graphic overview above to help you answer the following questions:**

   a. How did World War II create an industrial boom in California?

   ____

   b. How did the industrial boom affect the population of California?

   ____

2. **Read the red and blue headings on pages 251–253. List three groups who benefited from World War II.**

   a. ____________ ____________ ____________

   b. What kinds of opportunities do you think these groups experienced?

   ____

Name: ______________________ Date: ______________

CHAPTER 11

Lesson 1 Reading Strategy

California in Wartime

(*Oh, California* pp. 250–253)

Evaluate This reading strategy helps you recognize the difference between facts and opinions. A fact is something that can be proven to be true. An opinion is a belief based on what a person thinks or feels.

1. **Read from the section "War in the Pacific Causes Fear" on page 250. Circle the statement below that is an opinion.**
   a. Japanese Americans should not have been sent to internment camps.
   b. More than 100,000 Japanese Americans were sent to the camps.
   c. Internment camps were located far from the coast.

2. **Read from the heading "War Brings New Jobs and People" on page 251 up to the blue head "Opportunities for Women" on page 252. Write two facts about this section.**

   ____

   ____

3. **Read the section "Opportunities for Women" on pages 252–253. Then read this statement: During the war, some women took jobs in factories and at shipyards. Is this statement a fact or an opinion? Explain your answer.**

   ____

4. **Read the section "Opportunities for Black Americans" on page 252. Write two facts and two opinions about this section.**

Facts	Opinions
1.	1.
2.	2.

CHAPTER 11

Lesson 1 Summary

California in Wartime

(*Oh, California* pp. 250–253)

Summary also on Audiotape

Thinking Focus: How did World War II change life in California?

War in the Pacific Causes Fear

On December 7, 1941, Japanese planes bombed a United States military base at Pearl Harbor, Hawaii. The next day, the United States declared war on Japan. Americans were angered by the attack. Californians were upset and worried. Many feared Japan would attack them next. Some Californians held anti-Asian, and especially anti-Japanese, feelings. Some felt Japanese Americans on the West Coast would help Japan invade the United States.

These fears led the United States government to place Japanese Americans in internment camps. The camps were like prisons. They were located in the deserts of California, Arizona, Utah, and other places far from the coast. Over 110,000 Japanese Americans lived in these camps surrounded by barbed wire and soldiers.

Japanese Americans did not understand why they were held in camps. They were American citizens. They did not want Japan to invade the United States. In fact, many Japanese Americans fought bravely for the United States in World War II. The 442nd Regiment of Japanese Americans won many medals for their bravery.

? Why did World War II cause so much fear in California?

Summary continues on next page

War Brings New Jobs and People

During World War II, California played a big part in providing oil, food, and other supplies. The war helped California's **manufacturing** industry grow. One thing the country badly needed was ships. President Roosevelt asked Henry Kaiser, who had led the Hoover Dam project, to fill this need. Kaiser workers built nearly 700 ships at four **shipyards** in Richmond on the San Francisco Bay.

California factories also hired new groups of people:

- Before World War II, most factory workers were white men. But with many men in the armed forces, California needed workers. So factory jobs were offered to women. Women also served in the military. They drove jeeps, handled supplies, and worked in hospitals.
- Many companies did not hire black workers before the war began. But a presidential order made it unlawful to practice discrimination in war industries. So new jobs were offered to black Americans. In 1942, about 10,000 black Americans a month came to California. They formed new communities like Oakland near San Francisco and San Pedro near Los Angeles.
- Thousands of Mexican Americans served in the armed forces. Seventeen won the Congressional Medal of Honor. Many others received medals for bravery. After the war, some Mexican Americans bought homes and found jobs that were not open to them before the war.

? Why did factories hire new groups of workers during World War II?

manufacturing
(măn′yə-făk′chər-ĭng)
the process of turning materials into finished products

shipyard
(shĭp′yärd′)
a place where ships are built

Name: Date:

CHAPTER 11

Lesson 2 Preview

New Uses of Science and Technology

(*Oh, California* pp. 255–259)

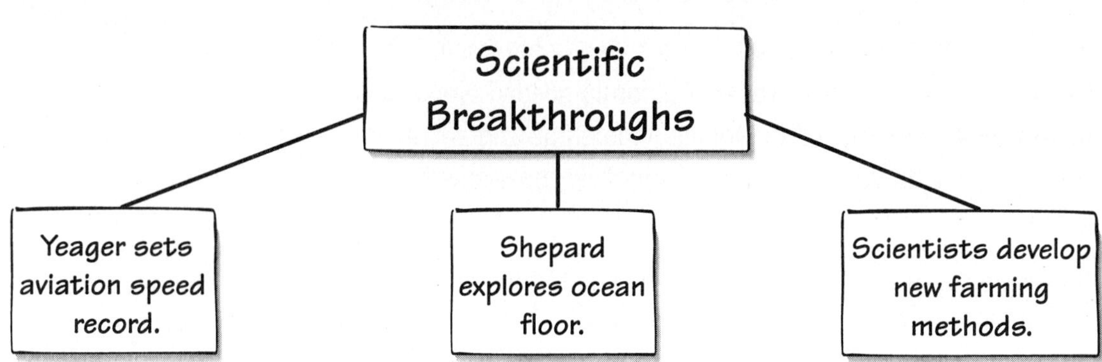
Science and Technology
Scientific Breakthroughs
Yeager sets aviation speed record.
Shepard explores ocean floor.
Scientists develop new farming methods.

1. **Look at the graphic overview above. Then answer the following question. What types of scientific breakthroughs will be discussed in this lesson?**

____

____

____

2. **Read the head "Aerospace History" on page 256. Then look at the pictures along the bottom of pages 256 and 257. What do you think the word *aerospace* refers to?**

____

____

Name: Date:

CHAPTER 11

Lesson 2 Reading Strategy

New Uses of Science and Technology

(*Oh, California* pp. 255–259)

Finding the Main Idea This reading strategy helps you organize and remember what you read. When you finish a selection, jot down the main idea and its supporting details.

1. **Read the section "Science Breaks Barriers" on page 256. Write *M* by the sentence that best tells the main idea of the section.**

   ___ California has many fine colleges and scientists.

   ___ New jets were tested at Edwards Air Force Base.

   ___ Aviation became a giant industry in California after World War II.

2. **Read the section "Diving to New Depths" on page 257. Write *M* by the sentence that best tells the main idea of the section.**

   ___ In 1964, Francis P. Shepard became the first American to see the ocean floor.

   ___ Jacques Cousteau built a new deep-sea submarine.

   ___ Francis P. Shepard went 800 feet down into the ocean.

3. **Write a supporting detail to the main idea: Francis P. Shepard explored the deep sea.**

   ____

4. **Read the section under "People and Machines Boost Agriculture" on pages 258 and 259. Then complete the chart.**

Main Idea	Supporting Details
	1.
	2.
	3.

CHAPTER 11

Lesson 2 Summary

New Uses of Science and Technology

(*Oh, California* pp. 255–259)

Summary also on Audiotape

Thinking Focus: How did new technology benefit California from 1945 to 1965?

Science Breaks Barriers

The jet airplane was invented near the end of World War II. The United States government chose Edwards Air Force Base in the California desert to test its new jets. California helped the new **aviation** age grow.

- California had colleges with scientists to help create better airplanes.
- California also had a manufacturing industry that could build the jets.

In 1947, a test pilot at Edwards Air Force Base named Chuck Yeager became the first person to fly faster than the speed of sound. But people hoped to go even faster and farther—into space. Rockets were built, and California's aviation industry got a new name. The name **aerospace** came from the words "spacecraft" and "airplane."

Francis P. Shepard spent almost 30 years off the coast of San Diego trying to find out what the bottom of the ocean looked like. But divers could not go down far enough to see the bottom. In 1964, Shepard became the first American to explore the ocean floor in a new, deep-sea submarine.

aviation
(ā´vē-ā´shən)
the building and flying of airplanes

aerospace
(âr´ō-spās´)
the science of designing, building, and flying aircraft and spacecraft

? In what ways did aviation and science grow and change in California after World War II?

Summary continues on next page

People and Machines Boost Agriculture

California has always needed workers to pick its crops. After World War II, this was still a problem. So, the bracero program was started. Under the program, Mexico provided braceros, or laborers, for California. The braceros traveled up and down the state with the seasons. In return, they received food, housing, and pay. The bracero program is not used today.

Science and technology also improved agriculture. Scientists worked to find cures for plant diseases. Research at universities also developed better farm machines. Together, people and machines make California's agriculture industry the largest and richest in the nation.

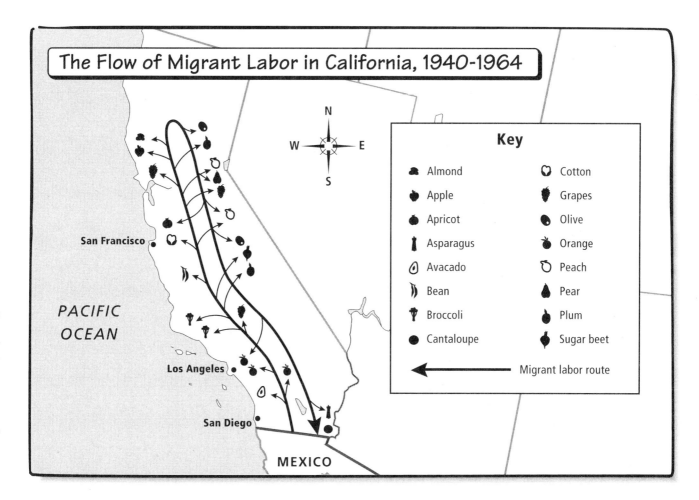

[?] How did California farming change after World War II?

Summary continues on next page

Name: Date:

CHAPTER 11

Lesson 3 Preview

New Ways of Living

(*Oh, California* pp. 260–263)

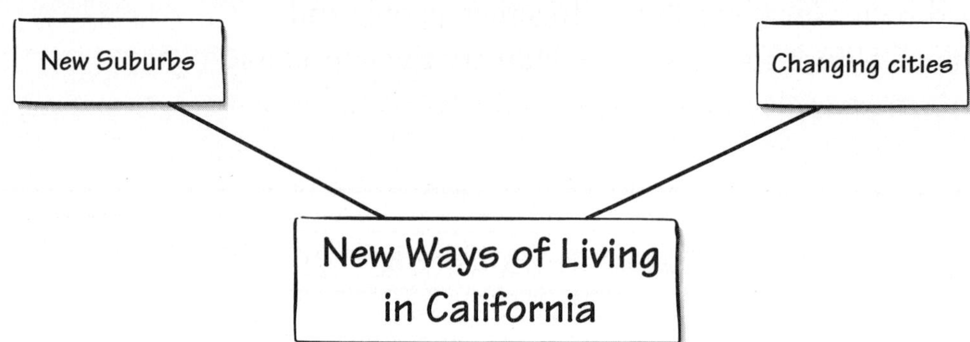

1. Look at the graphic overview. Then complete the following sentence:

After the war, ways of life changed for people living in the

______________________ and in the ______________________.

2. Look at the photograph at the top of page 261 and read the caption. What do the picture and caption tell you about the suburbs?

____

____

____

____

Name: Date:

CHAPTER 11

Lesson 3 Reading Strategy

New Ways of Living

(*Oh, California* pp. 260–263)

Compare and Contrast This reading strategy helps you understand how events are similar and different. As you read about historical events, think about how they compare and contrast with events you already know.

1. **Read the section "New Ways of Living" on page 260. Then fill in the chart below with information describing the ideas that came to pass and those ideas that did not.**

Things that Do Exist Today	Things that Do Not Exist Today

2. **Read the section "Growth of the Suburbs" on pages 261 and 262. Write a sentence describing the growth of California suburbs.**

3. **Read the section "Growth of the Cities" on pages 262 and 263. Write a sentence describing life in California cities.**

4. **Name one way that growth of suburbs was similar to growth of cities.**

5. **Describe differences between the suburbs and the cities in the 1960s.**

CHAPTER 11

Summary also on Audiotape

Lesson 3 Summary

New Ways of Living

(*Oh, California* pp. 260–263)

Thinking Focus: How was life in the suburbs different from life in the cities after World War II?

Growth of the Suburbs

The 1950s were a time of peace and progress. People wanted good jobs. They wanted to live in modern homes. Many thought California could offer this good life. Over a thousand people a day were moving to California. All these people needed homes. So builders began planning communities with hundreds of houses. These **suburbs** grew and spread out to cover areas that had once been farmland. Soon suburbs became small towns with their own stores and schools. People in the suburbs needed to get to their city jobs. So freeways were built. The state's first freeway was built in 1940. By the end of the 1950s, California spent a million dollars a day on new freeways.

suburb
(sŭb´ûrb´)
a community near a city

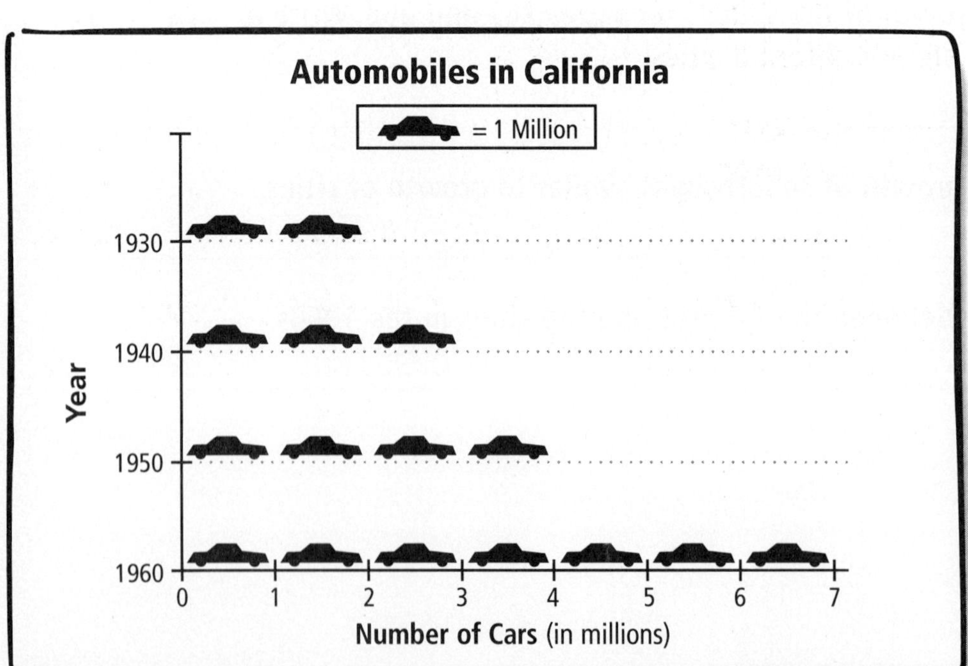

? What were the reasons for the growth of suburbs?

Summary continues on next page

Growth of the Cities

The many people who moved to California after World War II caused the cities to grow quickly. City neighborhoods were often made up of ethnic groups—black American, Armenian, Chinese, Jewish, Italian, Filippino, and Mexican. The East Los Angeles **barrio**, for example, grew into the world's third largest Mexican community. Here, most people spoke only Spanish. Mexican families wanted to live with other Mexicans. But discrimination forced many Mexican Americans to live in the barrio.

barrio
(bä′rē-ō′)
a Mexican American neighborhood

Black Americans were strongly discriminated against. They often lived in the worst areas. They got little money or help to improve their neighborhoods. Discrimination kept them from moving into the suburbs. Soon people began noticing the differences between life in the suburbs and life in the cities. Black Americans and other ethnic groups decided to save the culture of their communities and make them better places to live.

? What caused the barrios and other city neighborhoods to grow?

Summary continues on next page

Chapter Overview
New Steps Forward

Fill in the blank spaces below with information from the chapter.

When:
1960–1970s

Who:
African Americans, Native Americans, Mexican Americans, new immigrants

Californians Face Challenges

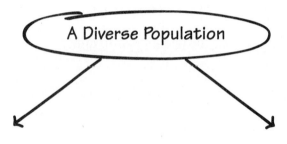

A Diverse Population

Civil ____________________ for all Californians.

____________________ bring cultural change.

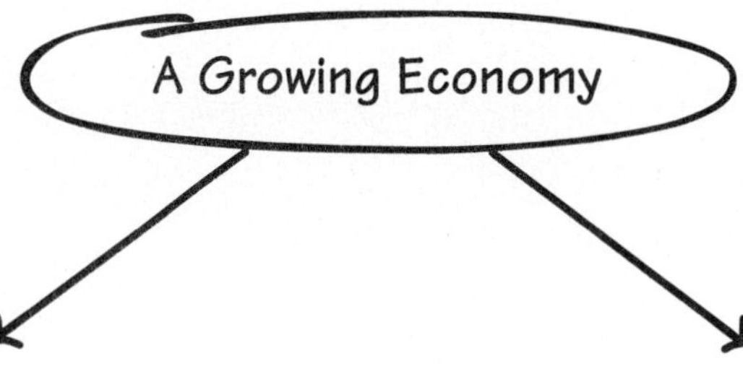

A Growing Economy

____________________ brings new trade.

____________________ helps people get jobs.

Name: ______________________ Date: ______________________

CHAPTER 12

Lesson 1 Preview

A Struggle for Rights

(*Oh, California* pp. 270–274)

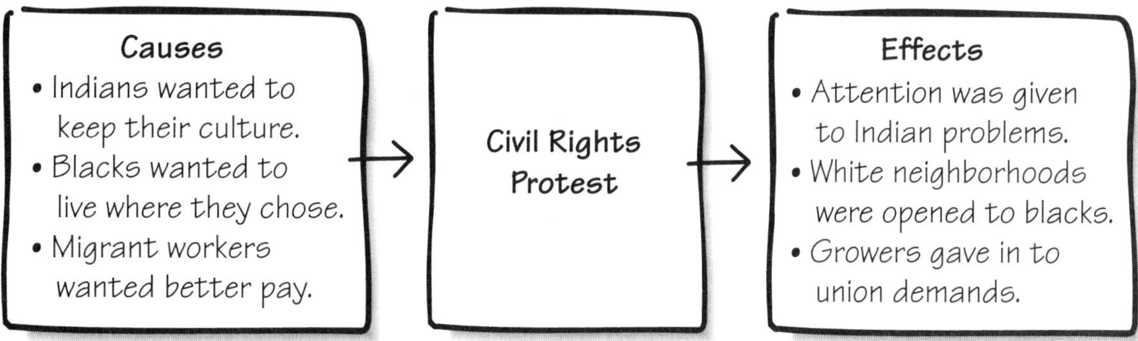

Causes and Effects of Civil Rights Protests
Causes
• Indians wanted to keep their culture.
• Blacks wanted to live where they chose.
• Migrant workers wanted better pay.
Civil Rights Protest
Effects
• Attention was given to Indian problems.
• White neighborhoods were opened to blacks.
• Growers gave in to union demands.

1. Study the graphic organizer above to complete the following sentences:

a. Because Indians protested to keep their culture, attention was given to ______________________.

b. Because black Americans protested about where they could live, ______________________ were opened to black Americans.

c. Because migrant workers protested for better pay, growers gave in to ______________________.

2. Look at the picture on page 271 in your text. Then find one other picture in the lesson that shows people protesting for their civil rights. Write a sentence telling what your picture shows.

____

____

____

____

____

____

____

Name: Date:

CHAPTER 12

Lesson 1 Reading Strategy

A Struggle for Rights

(*Oh, California* pp. 270–274)

Self-Question This reading strategy helps you stay focused on what you read. Ask yourself questions before you read a section. Then read to see if you can find the answer to your questions.

1. **Read the chapter title "A Struggle for Rights" on page 270. Then look at the picture and read the caption. Circle the letter of the question you think will be answered after reading this page.**
   a. How many Indians live in California?
   b. Why were the Indians on the island?
   c. Where is San Francisco?

   Read the section to see if the question you chose was answered.

2. **Read the heading "Blacks Seek Equal Rights" on page 271. Study the pictures on pages 271 and 272 and read the captions. Write a question about the heading and pictures.**

   ____

   Read pages 271–272 to see if the question you chose was answered.

3. **Read the heading "Farm Workers Organize" and the first paragraph on page 273. Write a question on the chart that you think this section will answer. Then read the section and write any answers you find.**

My Question	What I Learned by Reading

CHAPTER 12

Lesson 1 Summary

A Struggle for Rights

(*Oh, California* pp. 270–274)

Thinking Focus: What civil rights did minorities fight for during the 1960s and 1970s?

Blacks Seek Equal Rights

The laws passed in the 1940s and 1950s did not stop the unfair treatment of black Americans. In the 1960s, black Americans began to fight for their **civil rights**—their freedoms as citizens. For example, when a white person refused to sell a home to a black person, blacks and nonblacks decided to **protest**. They marched in the neighborhood until the owner agreed to sell the house. Groups also protested against businesses that would not hire black Americans. Most protests were peaceful. Some were not. In 1965, black protesters wrecked stores and set fire to houses in the Los Angeles neighborhood of Watts.

American Indians also protested unfair treatment. A group called "Indians of All Tribes" was angry because the government wanted to take away their lands. For two years, the Indians protested by setting up camp at Alcatraz, a deserted prison on an island in San Francisco Bay. Through their protest, the Indians got the nation's attention.

civil rights
(sĭv′əl rīts)
the freedoms entitled to all citizens

protest
(prə-tĕst′)
to show that one is against or disapproves of something

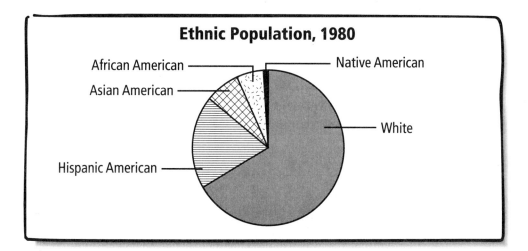

Ethnic Population, 1980

African American
Asian American
Hispanic American
Native American
White

Summary continues on next page

Blacks, Indians, and other **minority** groups wanted the same rights as everyone else. The work of ethnic groups and individuals in California and the rest of the country helped to bring about progress for minorities.

? How did protests help blacks win their civil rights?

Farm Workers Organize

Another group that faced discrimination was migrant workers. These laborers made low wages and often paid high rents and prices for food. Because the workers moved often, their children could not get good schooling.

Cesar Chávez and his sister-in-law Dolores Huerta went from town to town to organize the workers into a **labor union.** In 1965, Chávez organized a **strike.** He joined Filipinos who were already striking. Chávez asked grape pickers not to do any work until the grape growers agreed to the union's demands. Chávez then asked the public to **boycott** grapes.

Around the country, people refused to buy or eat grapes. In 1970, the grape growers finally agreed to give workers better pay and safer working conditions. But not all growers signed contracts with the unions. Today, the struggle for farm workers' rights continues.

? How did migrant laborers force owners to improve conditions for laborers on California's farms?

minority
(mə-nôr′ĭ-tē)
a group of people, like an ethnic group, that is a smaller part of the whole population

labor union
(lā′bər yo͞on′yən)
a group of workers who join together to protect their own rights

strike
(strīk)
to stop working in order to get better wages or working conditions

boycott
(boi′kŏt′)
to show support for a group by refusing to buy or use a product or service

Name: ______________________ Date: ______________________

CHAPTER 12

Lesson 2 Preview

A New Wave of Immigrants

(*Oh, California* pp. 276–279)

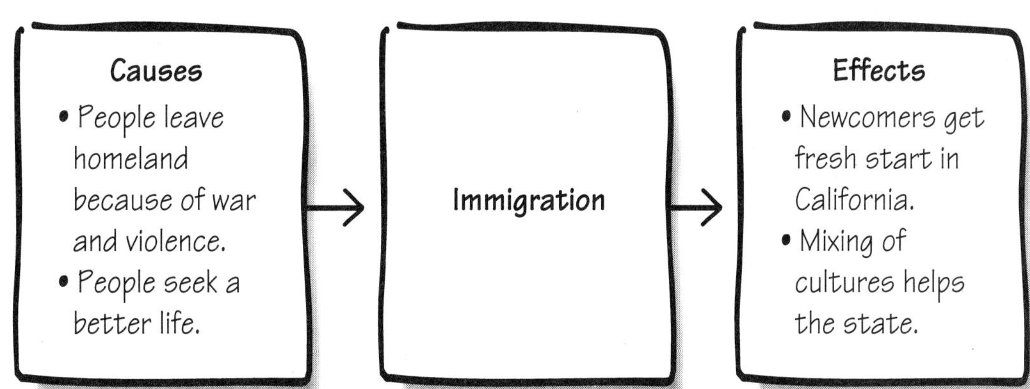

1. Study the graphic overview above to complete the statements below.

a. Many people forced from their homelands by ______________________ and ______________________ came to California seeking a better life.

b. In California, the mixing of cultures helps ______________________.

2. Look at the photo at the top of page 279 and read the caption. Then read the heading on the page. What is one cultural element that some immigrants bring with them from their homelands?

____

____

____

____

____

____

Name: Date:

CHAPTER 12

Lesson 2 Reading Strategy

A New Wave of Immigrants

(*Oh, California* pp. 276–279)

Cause and Effect This reading strategy helps you understand events and why they occur. As you read, think about the factors that caused an event. Then think about what the effects of that event may be.

1. Read page 276. What caused so many Hmong people to leave their country?

a. They thought it would be fun to live in California.

b. They had lost their homes during the war.

c. They were tired of village life.

2. Read the first two paragraphs of "The Nation Welcomes New Immigrants" on page 277. What was the effect of the law that allowed more people from Asia to enter the country?

a. The number of immigrants coming to the United States did not change.

b. A wave of Californians left the state to live in Pacific Rim countries.

c. Many new immigrants from these countries came to California.

3. What caused many of the hardships Asians faced in their countries?

____

4. Read the section "The Refugees of the War" on pages 277–278. Fill in the chart below to name the missing causes and effects.

Cause	Effect
People face war and unfair treatment by governments.	
	Many refugees die at sea.
The North America Free Trade Agreement (NAFTA) is signed.	

CHAPTER 12

Lesson 2 Summary

A New Wave of Immigrants

(*Oh, California* pp. 276–279)

Summary also on Audiotape

Thinking Focus: Why was the new wave of immigrants good for the newcomers and for California?

The Nation Welcomes New Immigrants

In 1965, the U.S. government passed a law that made it possible for many new immigrants to enter the United States. Many of these immigrants came from Southeast Asia and Central America.

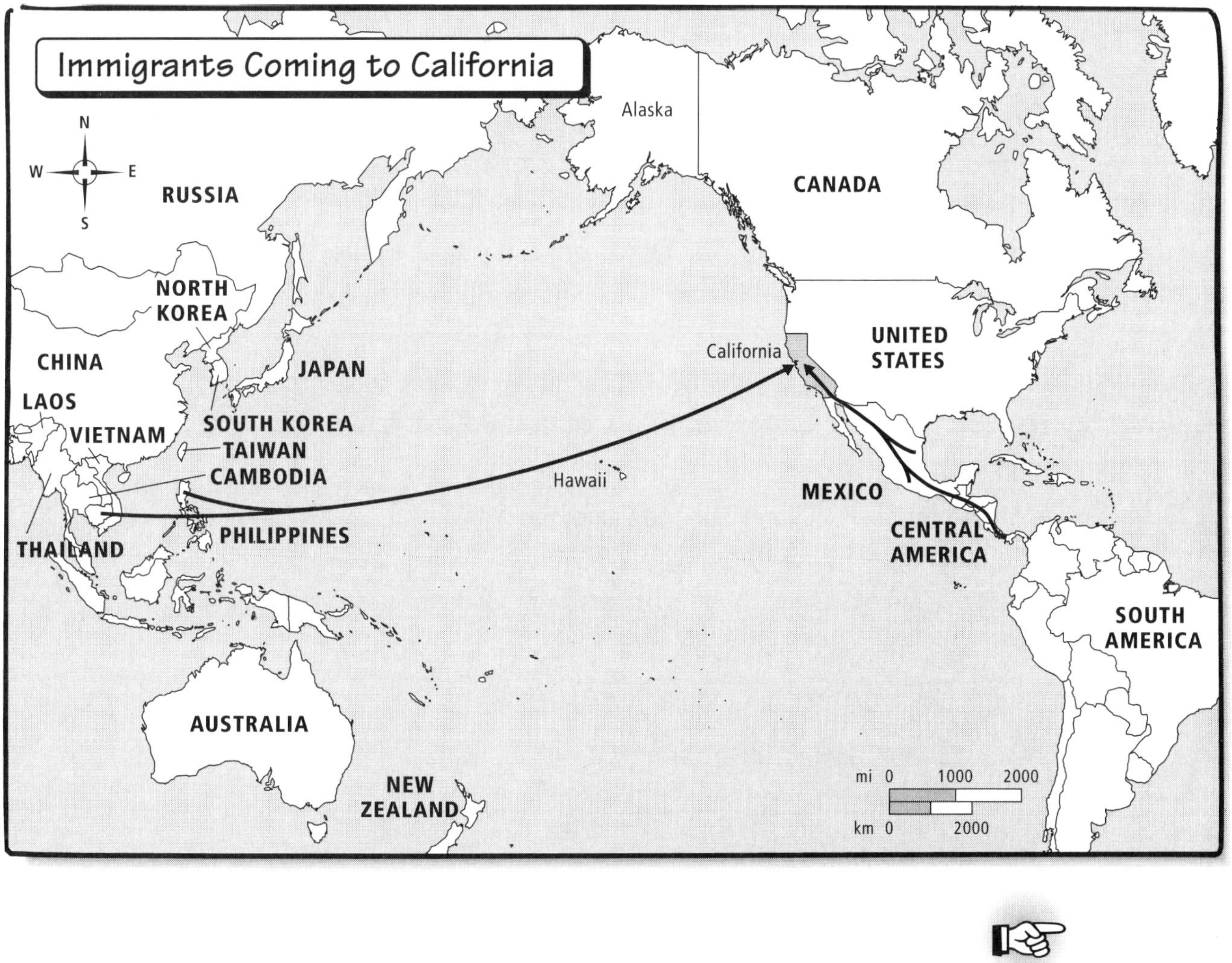

Immigrants Coming to California

Summary continues on next page

- During the 1960s and 1970s, the United States was involved in a war in the Southeast Asian country of Vietnam. The Vietnam War caused thousands of refugees to flee the area. These **refugees** faced a long voyage on small overloaded boats to find safety in countries like the United States. Many Hmong, a people of Laos, settled in California's Central Valley.
- Many refugees from Central America also left countries torn by war to begin new lives. People from countries such as Nicaragua and El Salvador traveled north through Mexico to reach California.

refugee
(rĕf'yo͞o-jē)
a person who flees his or her country to find safety or freedom

custom
(kŭs'təm)
a habit, tradition, or way of life that belongs to the people of one country or culture

Today, borders between California and Mexico are more open because of the North America Free Trade Agreement, or NAFTA. This agreement allows a greater flow of money and goods to cross borders in North American countries.

[?] Why did new immigrants pour into California after 1965?

Immigrants Enrich Culture

Immigrants from many lands have enriched the culture of California's cities and towns. Orange County has Vietnamese grocery stores and shops. Artesia, a town outside Los Angeles, sells candies, clothing, and jewelry from India. Japanese programs appear on a cable television station in Gardena, a city south of Los Angeles. Neighborhoods in Los Angeles have Korean churches. Like the immigrants who came before them, new immigrants have brought their **customs**, or way of life, to California. Their art, music, games, and dances make California an interesting place to live.

[?] What kinds of customs do immigrants bring to California?

Name: ______________________ Date: ______________________

CHAPTER 12

Lesson 3 Preview

A Growing California

(*Oh, California* pp. 284–287)

1. Read the graphic overview above and use it to complete each sentence below.

a. Industry grew and new jobs were created with the ______________________.

b. California's university system makes sure that minorities are assisted and workers are ______________________.

c. The ______________________ has brought new exports to market and increased business in California.

2. Look at the pictures at the top of page 285 and read the caption. How are computers used in your school?

____

____

____

Name: Date:

CHAPTER 12

Lesson 3 Reading Strategy

A Growing California

(*Oh, California* pp. 284–287)

Predit/Infer This reading strategy helps you understand what you have read and what you will read next. Before you read a section, think about titles, pictures, and captions. Then think about what will happen in the selection.

1. **Read the lesson title on page 284. Then look at the picture and read the caption. What industry do you predict the lesson will talk about? Check your answer.**

   ___ the ant industry

   ___ the computer industry

   ___ the farming industry

2. **Name a clue from the text that helped you make your prediction.**

   ____

3. **Read the heading "Technology and the Trade Boom." Then look at the pictures on page 285 and read the captions. What prediction can you make about California's trade boom? Check your answer.**

   ____

4. **How did your knowledge of California's industries help you make your prediction?**

   ____

5. **Read the head "Education Provides Opportunities" on page 287. Look at the picture and read the caption. Then complete the chart below.**

What I Know	What I Predict

CHAPTER 12

Lesson 3 Summary

Summary also on Audiotape

A Growing California

(*Oh, California* pp. 284–287)

Thinking Focus: In what ways have technology, trade, and education helped California to grow in the last 25 years?

Technology and the Trade Boom

The first computers were as large as your classroom. They were not used in schools or homes. Then, in 1959, the silicon chip was born in California. This chip is the brain of a computer. It holds millions of pieces of information, but is smaller than an ant. The silicon chip made it possible to build small personal computers.

During the 1970s and 1980s, computers brought a boom to California's industry. Soon, so many computer companies were located in the Santa Clara Valley south of San Francisco that the area was called "Silicon Valley."

Computers also helped California moviemaking grow. Talented young people found ways to use computers to make "special effects" like space creatures and spaceships on the movie screen.

California **exports** computers and films to other countries that want to buy these products. California also exports airplanes, oil, and farm products. In turn, California **imports**, or buys, from other countries, the products it needs. Cars, cameras, and silk are imported from countries like Japan, Korea, and Taiwan.

[?] Why are the computer and film industries important to California?

export
(ĕk'spôrt)
a product that is sold to another country

import
(ĭm'pôrt)
a product that is bought from another country

Summary continues on next page

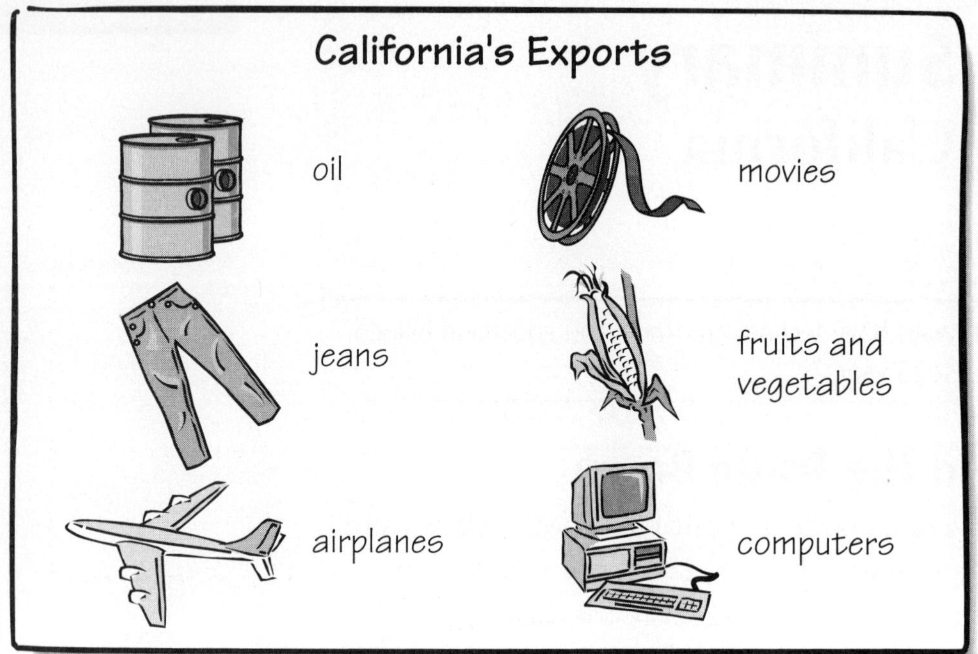

Education Provides Opportunities

Young people have played an important part in the success of California's industries. California leaders recognize this. They know that educating its young people is important to the growth and success of the state. Today, California has 20 universities, the largest system of higher education in the country. Lawmakers also realize that some people have trouble paying for a college education. In 1960, they passed a law to help these students. The law says that all high-school graduates with good grades can go to college, whether or not they have the money to pay for it.

[?] Why did California change its university system in 1960?

Chapter Overview
Decisions for the Future

Fill in the blank spaces below with information from the chapter.

When:
today

Where:
California

Who:
state government workers & citizens

California's Future

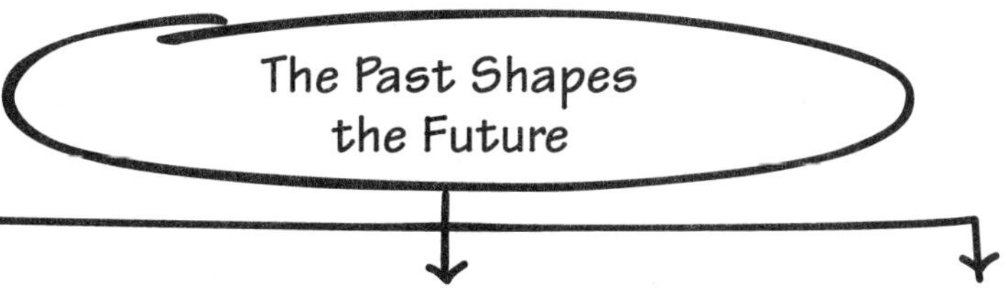

Los Angeles needs water.

____

Aqueduct causes conservation problems.

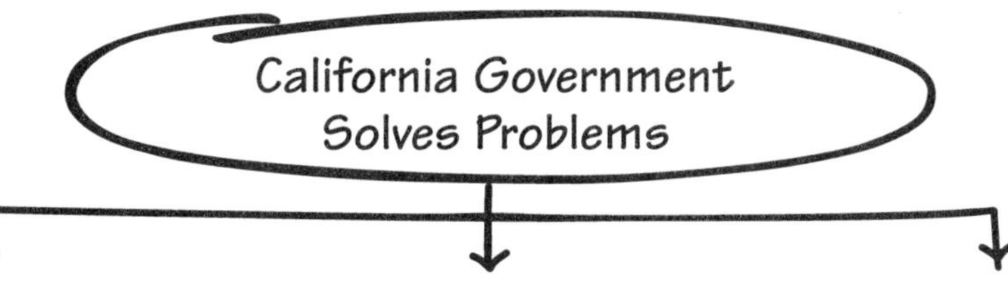

____

____

____

People Take Action to Solve State's Problems

individual action

____

Name: Date:

CHAPTER 13

Lesson 1 Preview

The Past Shapes the Future

(*Oh, California* pp. 292–295)

Los Angeles Water Supply

1906: Taking water
Los Angeles builds aqueduct to tap the Owens River; farms and ranches in the Owens Valley lose water supply.

→

1949: Taking more
Still growing and thirsty, the city extends its aqueduct north to Mono Lake; water level drops sharply, damaging the environment.

→

1989: Giving it back
Los Angeles agrees to share the Owens River and to take less water from Mono Lake; but city still needs new sources of water.

1. Look at the graphic organizer above. Then read the following pairs of events. Circle the letter of the event that happened first.

a. Los Angeles agrees to take less water from Mono Lake.
b. Los Angeles builds an aqueduct to tap the Owens River.
c. The water level in Mono Lake drops sharply.
d. Los Angeles agrees to share the Owens River.

2. Look at the pictures on page 293 in your text. Write a sentence to tell what happened to the Owens Valley when the Los Angeles Aqueduct was built.

Name: ______________________________ Date: ______________

CHAPTER 13

Lesson 1 Reading Strategy

The Past Shapes the Future

(*Oh, California* pp. 292–295)

Sequence This reading strategy helps you follow what is happening in your reading. As you read, pay attention to dates and times, as well as to words such as *before, finally, after,* and *then.*

1. **Read from "The Past Affects the Present" on page 293 to the bottom of the page. Place the events in order by writing 1, 2, and 3 in the blanks.**

   ___ Los Angeles built an aqueduct to bring in water from the Owens Valley.

   ___ After the aqueduct was built, dust storms became common in Owens Valley.

   ___ In the early 1900s, Los Angeles was a growing city that needed water.

2. **Read the section "The Water Search Continues" on page 294. Place these events in order by writing 1, 2, and 3.**

   ___ Los Angeles built an aqueduct to Mono Lake.

   ___ Mark Twain visited Mono Lake in the 1860s.

   ___ In 1941, Los Angeles was once again in need of water.

3.–4. **Read from "The Present Affects the Future" to the end of the lesson on page 295. Then complete the timeline below with dates and events.**

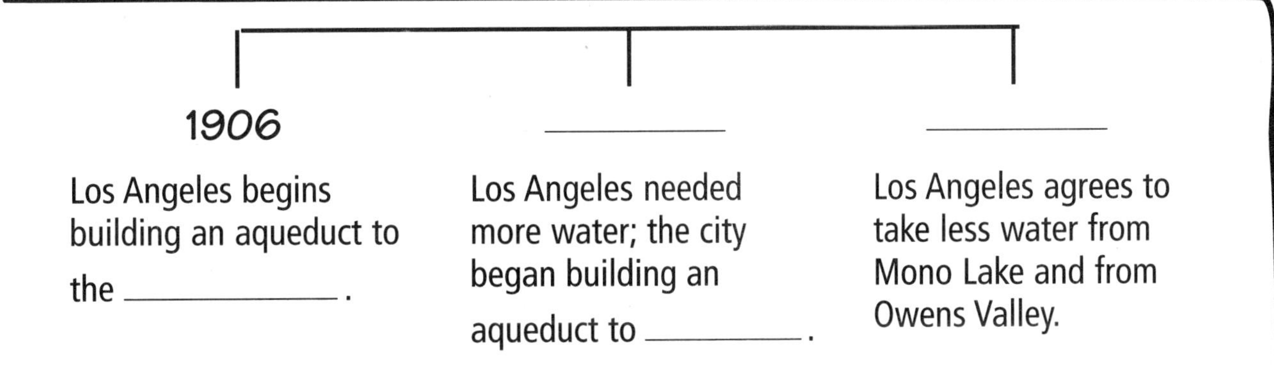

1906
Los Angeles begins building an aqueduct to the ____________.
____
Los Angeles needed more water; the city began building an aqueduct to ________.
____
Los Angeles agrees to take less water from Mono Lake and from Owens Valley.

CHAPTER 13

Summary also on Audiotape

Lesson 1 Summary

The Past Shapes the Future

(*Oh, California* pp. 292–295)

Thinking Focus: How has bringing water to Los Angeles affected the city's growth as well as California's environment?

The Past Affects the Present

Events in the past are often like a row of dominoes. If one domino falls, it makes another fall. The decision to build the Los Angeles Aqueduct in 1906 was like a falling domino. This aqueduct brought in water from the Owens Valley. The aqueduct supplied Los Angeles with the water it needed and helped the city grow. But without water, Owens Valley suffered. Dust storms swirled over the soil where cattle once grazed and crops once grew.

In 1941, Los Angeles once again needed more water. So the city built another aqueduct farther north to salty Mono Lake. This aqueduct took the water from four of the five freshwater

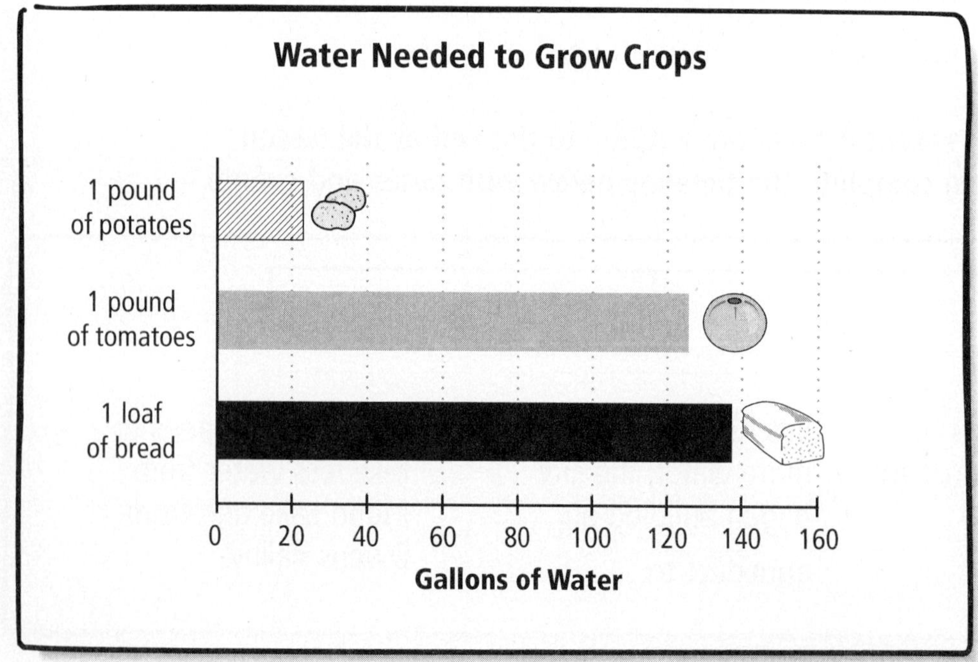

Summary continues on next page

streams that fed the lake. Soon the water level in the lake dropped. The lake became even saltier. The tiny shrimp in the lake began to die. This threatened the birds who depended on the shrimp for food. Few people knew how much the aqueduct would affect the **environment** around Mono Lake.

environment (ĕn-vī´rən-mənt) the soil, water, animals, plants, air, and other parts of nature that make up an area

conservation (kŏn´sûr-vā´shən) the protection of natural resources and the environment

[?] How did the loss of water change the environment of the Owens Valley and Mono Lake?

The Present Affects the Future

Today Californians think about **conservation** when they plan for the future. They try to protect the state's natural resources. In 1989, Los Angeles agreed to take less water from Mono Lake to help protect it. The city also promised to share some of the Owens River water with the people in Owens Valley. But where will Los Angeles get its water in the future? How can it get water without harming the environment?

Californians have made changes to improve their lives. Religious freedom and a good education are guaranteed. Some lands have been returned to Native Americans by the United States government. But California still has problems to solve. People disagree over natural resources. They argue for better working conditions. And, sadly, racism and discrimination have not disappeared.

[?] How will today's decisions on water conservation affect the future?

Name: Date:

CHAPTER 13

Lesson 2 Preview

California Government

(*Oh, California* pp. 296–300)

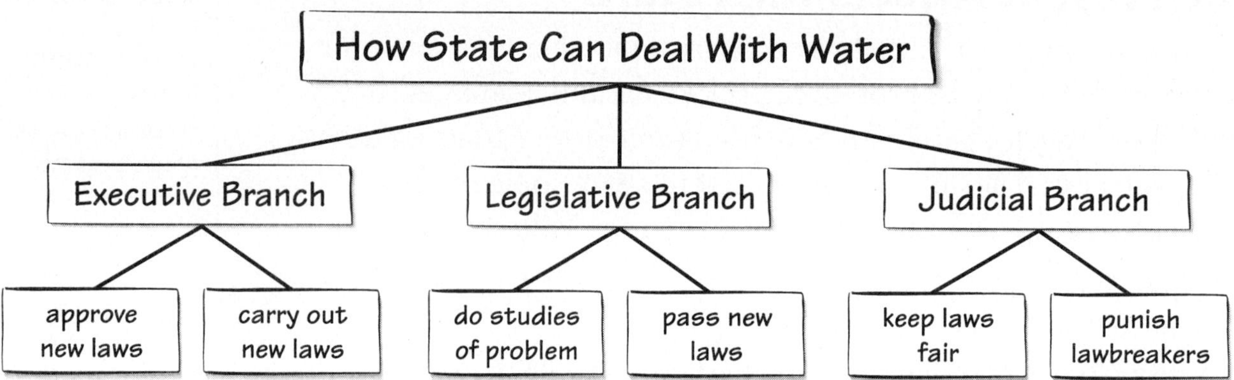

1. Look at the graphic overview above to learn how California can deal with its water problem. Then answer the questions below.

a. Which branch of government approves new laws and carries them out? ____________________

b. Which branch of government punishes lawbreakers?

____

c. Which branch of government studies the problems and suggests new laws? ____________________

2. Read the description of the three branches of government at the bottom of page 297. What do all three government branches work to do?

____

____

Name: Date:

CHAPTER 13

Lesson 2 Reading Strategy

California Government

(*Oh, California* pp. 296–300)

Think About Words This reading strategy helps you figure out the meaning of new words. When you come to an unfamiliar word, look for word parts you already know and use clues such as context and pictures.

1. **Read the section "How State Government Works" on pages 297–298. Then read this sentence: Most of the state's highest government *officials* work in Sacramento. What is an *official?***

   ____

2. **Name clues from your reading that could help you understand what an *official* is.**

   ____

3. **What does the word *approval* mean in this sentence?**
   If most of the legislators vote in favor of a suggested law, it is passed to the governor for *approval.* ______________________________

4. **Name clues that could help you understand what *approval* means.**

   ____

5. **Read the section "State Groundwater Problems" on pages 299 and 300. Then fill in as much of the chart as you can to figure out what the word *transport* means in this sentence:**
   Many landowners use the courts as a way to solve questions of rights to pump and transport groundwater.

WORD: transport

Clues from the reading: ______________________________

Clues from the pictures: ______________________________

Similar words I already know: ______________________________

Parts of words I already know: ______________________________

The word means:

CHAPTER 13

Lesson 2 Summary

California Government

(*Oh, California* pp. 296–300)

Thinking Focus: How does state government help solve problems?

How State Government Works

Like all other states, California has a state government. Thousands of people work in state government. But the highest officials work in the state capital, Sacramento. The state government runs prisons, builds schools, and handles the state's big problems, like water.

Today, water is California's most valuable resource. Some water comes from rivers, lakes, and reservoirs. But most comes from aquifers under the ground. Here, rainwater gathers in spaces among the soil, sand, and rock. The California government has passed laws to help manage the use of this water.

California's state government has three branches, or parts, that help make and enforce laws. These three branches are:

legislative branch (lĕj´ĭ-slā´tĭv brănch)
the part of government made up of the lawmakers who write bills

executive branch (ĭg-zĕk'yə-tĭv brănch)
the part of government made up of the governor and other departments who make sure state laws are carried out

governor (gŭv'ər-nər)
the highest official in a state government

judicial branch (jo͞o-dĭsh'əl brănch)
the part of government made up of the courts and judges

The Three Branches of Government

The Legislative branch	The Executive branch	The Judicial branch
The Legislative branch is made up of lawmakers elected by the citizens. These legislators help to make new laws. They also decide how the state will spend its money.	**The Executive branch** is headed by the **governor**. He or she approves new laws and makes sure all the state's laws are carried out.	**The Judicial branch** is made up of courts and judges. The judicial branch decides on the fairness of the state's laws. It also punishes people who break the law.

? Name the three branches of government and explain what each branch does.

Summary continues on next page

State Groundwater Problems

Early Californians got their water from streams, rivers, and lakes. But as more people settled in California, more water was needed. So people drilled into underground aquifers to get water. By the 1980s, some cities and towns were pumping out too much groundwater. The water levels in the aquifers dropped, and sea water seeped in. The water became unfit for drinking or watering crops. In other places, **pollution** made the water unsafe.

These problems led the state legislature to pass the Groundwater Management Act in 1992. This law lets local agencies plan how their community will use and protect its water resources. But the law has not solved all the water problems. The legislature is still looking for new solutions.

pollution
(pə-lo͞o´shən)
the destruction of land, air, and water due to the dumping of garbage and other harmful substances

[?] How is state government working to solve the groundwater problems in California?

You and State Government

Groundwater is not the only problem the state government looks at each year. The state government affects many other things you do. You can write to your state representative or senator to find out what state laws affect you and what the state is doing about issues that concern you.

State and national constitutions give citizens certain rights. When you are 18, you will be able to vote for government leaders. It will be your responsibility to choose the leaders who represent you. You will also have a say in how state problems are handled.

[?] What can you do to solve problems in California?

Name: Date:

CHAPTER 13

Lesson 3 Preview

People Take Action

(*Oh, California* pp. 302–305)

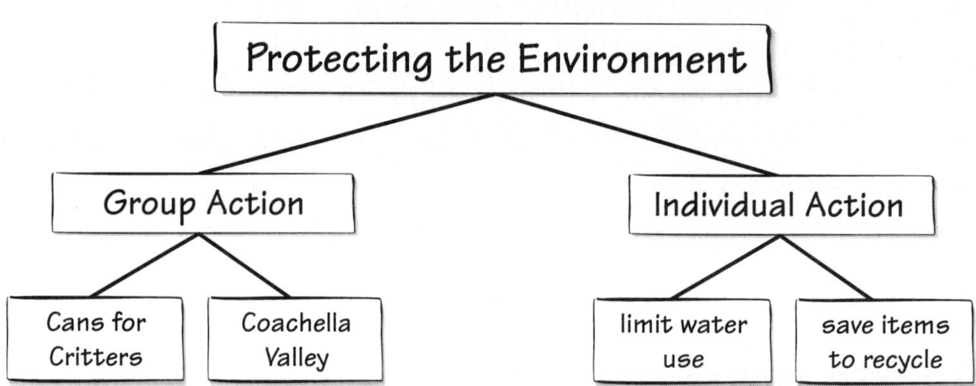

1. Look at the graphic overview above. Then use words from it to fill in the following outline.

I. Protecting the Environment

A. Group ______________

1. Cans for Critters
2. ______________

B. ______________ Action

1. Limit ______________
2. Save items to ______________

2. Read the lesson headings on page 303 and look at the lesson pictures. What kind of actions do you think you will read about in this lesson?

____

Name: Date:

CHAPTER 13

Lesson 3 Reading Strategy

People Take Action

(*Oh, California* pp. 302–305)

Using the Visuals This reading strategy helps you to use photographs, maps, charts, and illustrations to understand what you read. As you read, be sure to study the visuals and carefully read the captions.

1. **Look at the large photograph on page 302 and read the caption. What can you learn from this picture? Circle the best answer.**
   a. Condors are small birds.
   b. The San Diego Zoo is helping to raise baby condors.
   c. Condors live in the mountains.

2. **Look at the map on page 303 and read the caption. What can you learn from this map and its caption? Circle the best answer.**
   a. The Coachella Valley is in Mexico.
   b. Many different animals live in the Mojave Desert.
   c. The Coachella Valley Preserve is an area of land set aside for the fringe-toed lizard.

3. **Look at the two photographs on page 305 and read the captions.** Where is the Mt. Palomar observatory?

   ____

4. **Look at "A Closer Look" on page 304 and read the captions. Complete the chart to tell what you learned about helping the environment.**

What I Learned

CHAPTER 13

Lesson 3 Summary

People Take Action

(*Oh, California* pp. 302–305)

Summary also on Audiotape

Thinking Focus: In what ways can individuals and groups work to improve California's future?

The Power of Many People

People in state government work to solve problems. But you don't have to be in government to get things done. For example, people in Coachella Valley in southern California worked together to solve a problem.

By 1980, the building of homes, hotels, and golf courses in the area made the fringed-toed lizard an **endangered species.** Some people wanted to save the lizard. But others wanted to build more homes for people moving into the area.

Finally, builders, government officials, people living in the valley, and environmental groups worked together to come up with a plan. They set aside some of the land for building and some of the land for the lizard. The agreement was so good that it set an example for groups all over the country.

endangered species
(ĕn-dān′jərd spē′shēz)
an animal or plant that is in danger of disappearing from the earth

[?] How did different groups benefit from the Coachella Valley solution?

Summary continues on next page

The Power of One Person

As a California fourth-grader, there are many ways you can help make your state a better place to live. Think of an issue you care about, such as the environment—the land, water, and air around you. Then do something to help solve the problem on your own. For example:

How You Can Make a Difference

Recycle bottles, cans, and paper.

Ride your bike instead of getting a ride.

Write a letter to your representatives or to your local newspaper.

Conserve water.

[?] How can people's decisions affect the future of California?